# SUBTERRANEAN
# NORWICH

## The grain of the city

## *Matthew Williams*

*Lasse*
*Press*

First published 2017
by the Lasse Press
2 St Giles Terrace, Norwich NR2 1NS, UK
www.lassepress.com
lassepress@gmail.com

ISBN-13: 978-0-9933069-4-5

Typeset in Garamond and Trade Gothic by
Curran Publishing Services Ltd, Norwich, UK

Printed in the UK by Cambrian Printers, Aberystwyth.

# Contents

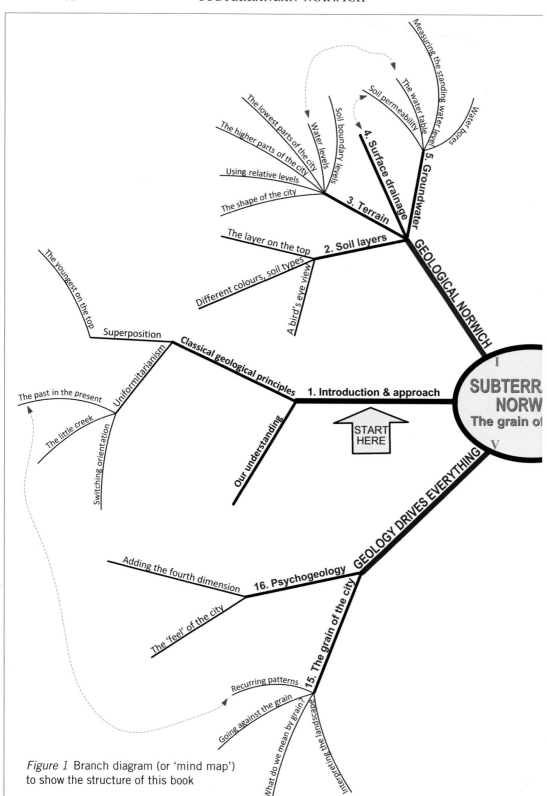

*Figure 1* Branch diagram (or 'mind map')
to show the structure of this book

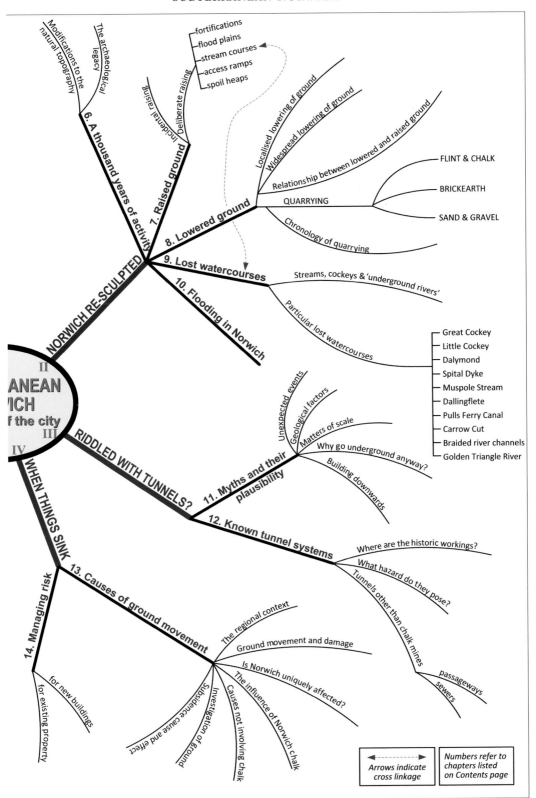

fortifications
flood plains
stream courses
access ramps
spoil heaps

Modifications to the natural topography
The archaeological legacy
6. A thousand years of activity
Incidental raising
Deliberate raising
7. Raised ground
8. Lowered ground

Localised lowering of ground
Widespread lowering of ground
Relationship between lowered and raised ground
QUARRYING
Chronology of quarrying

FLINT & CHALK
BRICKEARTH
SAND & GRAVEL

NORWICH RE-SCULPTED

9. Lost watercourses
10. Flooding in Norwich

Streams, cockeys & 'underground rivers'
Particular lost watercourses

Great Cockey
Little Cockey
Dalymond
Spital Dyke
Muspole Stream
Dallingflete
Pulls Ferry Canal
Carrow Cut
Braided river channels
Golden Triangle River

II
ANEAN
ICH
f the city
III
IV

RIDDLED WITH TUNNELS?

Unexpected events
Geological factors
Matters of scale
11. Myths and their plausibility
Why go underground anyway?
Building downwards

12. Known tunnel systems

Where are the historic workings?
What hazard do they pose?
Tunnels other than chalk mines
passageways
sewers

WHEN THINGS SINK

13. Causes of ground movement

The regional context
Ground movement and damage
Is Norwich uniquely affected?
The influence of Norwich chalk
Causes not involving chalk
Investigation of ground
Subsidence cause and effect

14. Managing risk
for new buildings
for existing property

Arrows indicate cross linkage

Numbers refer to chapters listed on Contents page

# Figures and boxes

## Boxes

These contain more detailed information or act as an aside to the main text.

# Foreword

One of the sections in Matthew Williams's fascinating and most informative book is entitled 'Geology drives everything'. It forms the conclusion of the volume and, by the time that we reach this point, the statement has long ceased to sound like the sort of hyperbole that one expects from a man passionate about his discipline. Instead, it has become a self-evident statement, so compelling is the evidence presented of the importance of geology to an understanding of both where and how we live – and how that existence has developed through time.

*Subterranean Norwich* is very much focused on the East Anglian city, notably the historic core of Norwich within the medieval city walls. However, it can be read with reference to the growth of any community and the relationship of that community to the landscape around and beneath it. The methodological approach is one that is clearly of wide applicability and so, while this book will surely find a good local audience, we must hope that it will be picked up as a primer for similar investigations across the country.

The strengths of the book lie first in its carefully inclusive text which marries basic geological principles to investigation – both geological and archaeological – and to lived experience. Second, though, the text is gloriously embellished by the many images to which it is linked throughout the volume. Indeed, as 'a picture is worth a thousand words', this book thereby becomes a weighty treatise transmuted into a most readable, and easily comprehensible, volume.

There is much to learn here. Sections on natural processes linked to water, soil permeability, drainage, watercourses and flooding are complemented by discussion of human impact upon the landscape – chapters beguilingly labelled 'raised ground' and 'lowered ground' for instance explore the many ways in which the topography of the city has been shaped over a millennium and more. Indeed, the linkage between geological and archaeological study of the urban landscape, adding to understanding in both disciplines, forms one of the major lessons of the book. An archaeologist must have some comprehension of the geology of an area in order to appreciate human impact, while a geologist needs to bear in mind the drivers behind human activity to explain alterations to natural horizons.

Matthew Williams emphasises this interdisciplinarity by insisting on viewing Norwich in four dimensions – in essence, length, breadth and depth with time added. He even supplies a fifth dimension when, through 'pyschogeology', he explores perceptions of space within the city. This is 'emotional landscape', encouraging an empathetic approach to the urban environment. His marvellous book, with its judicious illustrations, does just that – we emerge with a sharpened awareness of how integrated the built city is with its underlying geological skeleton. He encourages us to look at the city, with empathy and comprehension. His book is a wonderful gift of knowledge to all who wish to understand the places in which they live.

Brian Ayers
former County Archaeologist for Norfolk
Research Fellow and Honorary Senior Lecturer, University of East Anglia

# Biographical note

Matthew Williams is a chartered geologist with a professional background in the construction industry. He has worked predominantly in East Anglia, and has intensive experience in the Norwich area.

He was born in Hertfordshire but grew up from the age of 10 in Norwich. He left the city in the mid-1970s to go to university and never expected to come back. But after graduating and a spell with Blue Circle Cement at various UK production sites he returned in 1981 to Norwich to join May Gurney & Company as a geotechnical engineer. He worked on a number of local construction projects, including the new Magistrates Court and Dencora House, and oversaw the ground investigation work for the A11 Thetford bypass and other trunk roads.

In 1988 he left May Gurney to jointly set up an independent site investigation company, SIC (East Anglia) Limited, which was run as a co-operative and traded successfully for 22 years. Over that period he oversaw exploratory ground investigations on over 2,000 different sites throughout East Anglia, several hundred of which were located in the city, to include some major projects such as The Forum, the Cathedral extensions, St Anne's Wharf and the old Mann Egerton site. Along the way, Matt completed a Master's degree in European traffic engineering and now works as a national standard cycle instructor for Smart Cycle Training.

He maintains his passion for matters subterranean by adult tutoring for WEA and talks to various local groups. No longer earning a living in the geotechnical industry, he says he is acutely aware of a wide gulf between fanciful accounts of Norwich ground conditions regularly put out by the media and the detailed knowledge kept under wraps by the engineering professionals. So as a lover of the 'fine city', his mission is to help bring into the public domain a more informed view of subterranean Norwich and its implications for us all.

# Preface and acknowledgements

This book is essentially a journey through Norwich, but not necessarily a linear one.

Your journey will probably be assisted if you equip yourself with a decent street map to use alongside the book, preferably one showing the central area in one view, such as the *Norwich A–Z*.

Many books have been published about this fine and fascinating city, and most of them adopt a reasonably logical and ordered approach.

Many of the publications featuring photos of 'Old Norwich' have chapters organised around different quarters of the city, as if the reader is spending an afternoon wandering around each looking at particular buildings or viewpoints. This builds up an essentially **two-dimensional** representation of the city, the way most of us know the place through our experience moving around, supported occasionally by reference to maps or phone apps. It is particularly enriching when you as local reader are taken along a route or down an alleyway you realise you are not familiar with.

The books illustrating old postcard views are necessarily a little more random in their approach, darting around according to the availability of picturesque views, sometimes grouping these according to themes such as 'the river' or 'the Cathedral'. On the other hand, George Plunkett, having accumulated a more comprehensive collection of photographs of buildings, was able in his excellent books to offer a systematic journey along each side of a given street, more reminiscent of the approach of the Domesday medieval surveyors, or the later directories like *Kelly's*.

My personal work experience investigating ground conditions in and around Norwich means in theory I am able to add a **third dimension** to our understanding of the city – not only of the layers of soil (and other features) beneath the surface, but crucially relating them to the topography of the city, which is anything but flat and level. Having an appreciation of the 'ups' and 'downs' (especially when you are able to express these in numerical terms) is a powerful tool for understanding the city.

Books or essays concentrating more on the historical development of the city will obviously tend to follow a time-line, perhaps from the early settlements in the area through the medieval establishments, then via the later industrial stages of the city's history and its cultural development right up to the present. The chronological **fourth dimension** thus tends to subordinate the other dimensions, but brings them in as necessary to explore, for example, the two-dimensional spatial development of the city through time, or the three-dimensional build-up of archaeological layers over the centuries of occupation.

My thesis, starting as a geologist, is that much of the development of the city we know today can ultimately be traced back to the **natural geology and topography** – explaining among other things:

♦ the reasons that Norwich is here (as opposed to somewhere else)
♦ the significance of drainage courses
♦ the position and layout of the occupied areas
♦ the specific locations of quarrying
♦ the alignment of roads and parish boundaries
♦ the factors influencing repeated human interventions, right up to the present.

This underlying physical make-up of the land is what I refer to in my subtitle as 'the grain of the city'.

My time frame is relatively long, stretching back considerably earlier than most archaeological studies, to a period when the climate may have been very different and the landscape not yet suited to occupation by human beings.

Adding to this my interest in transport and development, I have been bold enough to try to project this thesis forward in time in order to seek to understand what a sustainable Norwich could look like in the future, that is if we plan land-use and transportation to go with the grain rather than against it. I am making the assumption here that 'sustainability' involves breaking away from the high-carbon dependency that has to some extent distorted our city's spatial development over the last century and arguably made certain aspects of urban life increasingly dysfunctional.

What we are therefore pursuing is a **holistic, four-dimensional model** for understanding Norwich.

I cannot necessarily promise a linear, systematic journey through what is inevitably a multidimensional subject. It is however worth the pursuit, and we shall be looking, often below the ground, for connecting aspects that explain recurring patterns through time in given areas of the city. I hope you will discover some subterranean facts and principles that will not only enhance your appreciation of a great heritage, but also inform you if you are making plans for the future.

## Acknowledgements

I would like to express my gratitude to all those who have assisted me, knowingly or otherwise, in the preparation of this book.

Much of my detailed understanding came about as the result of the efforts of my work colleagues Chris Edwards and Ed Thomsett over more than 20 years, supplemented by generous conversations with other toilers in the ground back then and since.

The IT help received from David Pearce helped get me going during the early stages of trying to make a book out of adult education course material. Along the way, several friends offered wise advice, and I am grateful for the patience Susan Curran has shown to this rookie writer as we moved towards the final draft.

In a picture-heavy publication I must of course express thanks to those individuals and organisations who have kindly allowed use of illustrations. Full picture credits are to be found on page 153.

This book is not intended as a definitive technical treatise, but I am nevertheless hoping the worst of my mistakes were found before it went to print, thanks to the checking and proofreading work of more than one person. Here, I need to thank Paul Simmonds, Brigid Purcell and my wife Amanda. Needless to say, the responsibility for any errors or omissions that remain is mine alone, and I would certainly wish to correct these in the event of any future editions.

Matthew Williams
Norwich, 2017

# 1
# Introduction and approach

If you know Norwich, just how well do you know it? If the answer is 'not very well', then this book is one way to make a start, albeit taking a slightly unusual angle on the city.

If on the other hand you are a resident or a frequent visitor, you will be lucky enough to have a working knowledge of the layout of the city, probably in the form of a mental map. You will recognise the historic core within the present ring road, asymmetrically shaped in plan a bit like a turnip,[1] beyond which is more concentric development to the outer ring road in the form of a clock, then patchy later sprawl stretching the city edge west and east along the line of the A47 southern bypass. With the building of the Northern Distributor Road, considerable future expansion is undoubtedly taking place on the north side of the city, further modifying our conception of the urban layout, generating yet more areas of nebulous suburban development.

Our mental map probably adopts the convention of placing north at the top of the page, so it's sometimes helpful to get a disorientated visitor to navigate by traversing an imaginary clock face where Norwich Castle is at the centre and the outer ring road is the clock rim. The suburban village of Eaton, for example, is located just outside the rim at 8 o'clock (see Figure 2). The clock would have been an even more straightforward conception less than a century ago when virtually all of Norwich was neatly confined within a circular ring road linking together the radial roads – which could be regarded as spokes of a wheel.

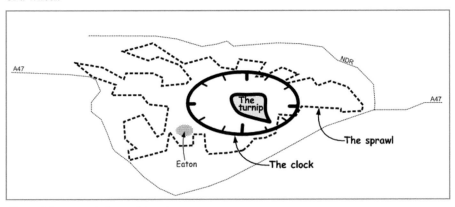

*Figure 2* Conceptual shape of the city

So much for our two-dimensional understanding. What about the third dimension, the bit beneath our feet? For people who may have lived here for years, this hidden aspect often remains buried in mystery and mystique. The hint of something uncertain in the ground has caused many to prevaricate over a property purchase in this part of the world,

---

1   Or as William Smith described it in 1807, 'the general shape of the city may not be unaptly compared to that of a very short and broad shoulder of mutton'.

and the invisibility of what lies beneath has certainly been a boon to newspaper journalists needing to fill column inches on every occasion that any hole has opened up in a city road.

One purpose of this book is to help bridge the wide gap between what is actually known about 'ground level downwards' and the more speculative hyperbole that is not uncommonly seen in print concerning Norwich in particular.

And there is at least one further dimension we must consider: the fourth dimension, of time. Norwich is nothing if not a historic city, and by definition things change over time. Understanding how underground conditions may have been affected by a thousand years or more of human occupation (to say nothing of the few hundred thousand years before that) adds enrichment to our understanding and appreciation of this fine city.

I would go further, and argue that an understanding of the fundamental relationship between ground conditions and urban development over many years could be the soundest basis for planning a sustainable future for the city – and that principle probably applies for most cities, not just the particular one in question.

The approach that will be taken in this book is therefore to develop what could be described as a rational 'four-dimensional model' for subterranean Norwich, and seek to make this as 'holistic' as possible to cover as many aspects of urban living as we can. Along the way we shall apply to our model a few well-established traditional geological principles, notably uniformitarianism ('the past in the present') and superposition ('the youngest on the top'). See Boxes 1 and 2 for further illustration of these principles.

The intention is to use this rational model to explore in turn the themes represented by the first four parts of this book: *Geological Norwich, Norwich resculpted, Riddled with tunnels?* and *When things sink,* and there will inevitably be some overlap or interchange between these areas, as suggested by the double-ended arrows on the branch diagram (Figure 1).

The final part, slightly provocatively titled *Geology drives everything,* is intended to stimulate thinking about how the ground conditions may ultimately have affected how the city we see today has developed, and where things might go from now. I also speculate on the degree of linkage not only to how people behave, but also to how they feel about Norwich. This is to respond to what appears to be a recent growing interest in 'psychogeography', a subject which lends itself to the work of writers and artists in a city of culture.

Fear not, for the most part the idea of the book is to remain practical and pragmatic. So if you already have a stake in the city, you may well find the information herein provides an interesting context for day-to-day situations and decision making. If you are only just making acquaintance, I hope the book will help you discover a few early pointers as to why the city is as it is.

And to curious readers from elsewhere in the world: welcome! There is even more reason to pay Norwich your first visit. The hope is that once you've arrived, scratched the surface and delved a little deeper, you will be sufficiently fascinated to come back again for more.

Box 1

## *Classical geological principles 1:* **Uniformitarianism**

### The past in the present

This theory was originated by James Hutton in the 1700s but formalised by another Scottish geologist Charles Lyell in the 1830s in his *Principles of Geology*. He argued that geological remains are explainable by processes we can observe somewhere on the Earth today, or to put it another way, 'the present is the key to the past'.

Here are two examples of the past re-emerging from subterranean Norwich and having an influence on the present.

### The little creek

Many people love the work of the Norwich School of Artists, a group of painters who worked in and around the city during the first three decades of the nineteenth century. Its most famous member was John Crome, and he painted a number of scenes in the vicinity of New Mills, a weir across the River Wensum in the west part of the city centre. In one painting dated 1812, entitled *New Mills: men wading*, we are on the downstream side of the mill looking diagonally across the Wensum, which flows out of view to the right (see Figure 3). In the centre background amongst timber-framed houses we can see a little bridge crossing a creek. However if we go to the same viewpoint today there is no creek, just a steel-piled river wall with modern houses and apartments beyond (Figure 4). Luckily we have a range of historic maps of Norwich, and if we look at Cole & Roper's map of around 1807, sure enough, the creek is shown exactly at the position Crome painted it (Figure 5).

*Figure 3 New Mills: Men Wading by John Crome, 1812*

Later maps show us that the creek had disappeared a couple of decades later beneath industrial development.

Fast forward to the mid-1990s and a further redevelopment of land off the west side of Coslany Street with three-storey housing. A mid-twentieth-century light industrial building has been demolished and a digger is working to remove old drains from a concrete yard. The dark-coloured soil being excavated

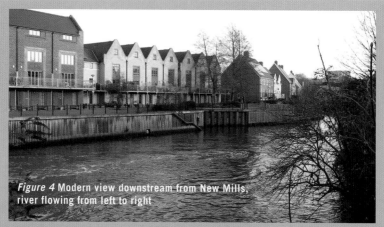

*Figure 4* Modern view downstream from New Mills, river flowing from left to right

contains some brick and flint rubble, then suddenly the digger bucket strikes something more substantial – some sort of underground structure, but what? Further careful excavation around the obstruction reveals – the arch of a bridge (Figure 6). It is almost certainly the same bridge depicted by John Crome all those years ago, subsequently buried for more than a century. Sadly, it had to be broken up and removed

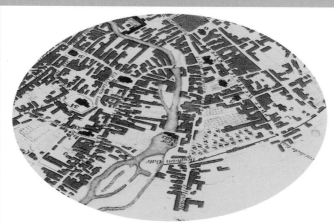

*Figure 5* Extract from Cole & Roper's map of Norwich of c.1807, rotated to look towards the south-east, with a side creek visible on the farther (downstream) side of New Mills

from underground to allow the piled foundations of the new houses to be installed, but at least we know now what it was.

## Switching orientation

On the opposite side of the city from New Mills, the River Wensum runs through low-lying marshland to the east of the ancient north–south route known as King Street. As the medieval city expanded, the river frontage was exploited as wharfs for mooring,

*Figure 6*
Old bridge
uncovered
during work
at Coslany
Street,
September
1993

with ready access to the buildings fronting onto the street. One of these buildings was Dragon Hall (Figure 7), a surviving merchant's hall built around 1428, but occupying a site that had been in use for several hundred years before then, as proved by archaeo-logical excavation carried out prior to its conversion to a heritage centre, and more recently a writers' centre. An interesting observation on the archaeological plans is that the outbuildings to the rear of Dragon Hall have not always been built square to the main building. Some are at an angle up to 10 degrees from being square to the street frontage (Figure 8). This is thought to be because at various stages in its history, new building work was focused on the river frontage at the rear of the plot, which is not quite parallel to the road at the front, with the result that the angles kept switching.

Immediately to the north of Dragon Hall is a site known as St Anne's Wharf. Until construction of flats started in 2016 this site had remained undeveloped since closure of the Watney Mann brewery in 1985, which was finally demolished down to ground level in 2008 (Figure 9). This had included a bottle store constructed in the 1970s, and because of the marshy ground, that sizeable building had been built on a heavy grid of concrete piles and ground beams aligned to the King Street frontage, where there was a substantial retaining wall. The site had waited years for redevelopment because of a range of difficult planning factors. One of the factors was the architectural aspiration to construct new residential and commercial buildings fronting onto the river, and for economic reasons it was desirable to seek to reuse the existing underground piles rather than remove them and install new ones. Unfortunately these piles were arranged in lines parallel to the road, which is about 10 degrees different from the line of the river frontage. So you can see how the orientation-switching process that has gone on for centuries continues into the present!

You could regard this as another manifestation of the Principle of Uniformitarianism.

*Figure 7* Dragon Hall, photographed in the late 1990s before conversion

*Figure 9* Watney Mann Brewery site during demolition, April 2008

*Figure 8* Dragon Hall archaeological excavation, 1998

Box 2

## Classical geological principles 2: *Superposition*

### The youngest on the top

This theory was first proposed by the Danish scientist Nicholas Steno in the 1600s, and was incorporated by Charles Lyell into his *Principles of Geology* published the 1830s. He stated that in layers of soil, the stratum that is on the bottom is older than the stratum on the top (Figure 10).

A few years ago a committee was established to investigate and systematically record the parish records held by churches in Norfolk. These contain priceless social history dating from medieval times, and there was a fear this could become lost. In some churches, there are great ancient timber storage chests into which annual churchwardens' records had been dropped as bound packets of papers for many decades, even centuries. The process of recording these archives consisted literally of excavating down through the layers of papers. At what level can we expect the oldest records to be found? Self-evidently at the bottom, and that is the essence of the principle of superposition (Figure 10).

Perhaps unsurprisingly, in the world of geology, exceptions are occasionally to be found, usually when layered sequences of soil or rocks have unexpectedly been folded over by later tectonic earth movements or the pressure of glacier ice, which can result in putting the older layers uppermost. Examples of such glaciotectonic sequences can be found in the cliffs of North Norfolk (Figure 11). To Steno and Lyell's credit, the principle when stated is usually conditioned on it being 'a vertical sequence of undisturbed strata'.

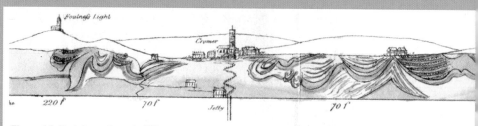

*Figure 11* Sketch section of cliff exposure between Cromer and East Runton, by Samuel Woodward, 1833

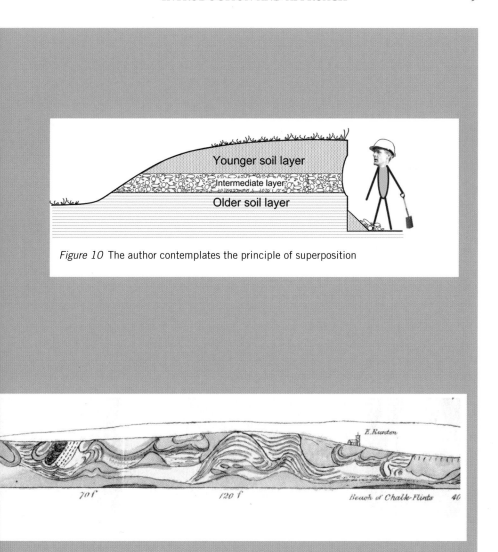

*Figure 10* The author contemplates the principle of superposition

*Figure 12* South-eastward aerial view of the city centre, with the orange blob of soil at Chapelfield in 2003 gradually turning grey as development proceeds

# Part I

# Geological Norwich

*Figure 13* Temporarily exposed cross-section of strata at Palace
Street, 2006, showing (from the top down) fill, river gravel,
chalk and the water table

# 2
# Soil layers

In this first part, we are concentrating on the soil layers that have sat quietly at depth for millennia, long before the human settlement that became Norwich ever came into existence. I say 'quietly', but of course things may have been a bit noisy when glacial meltwater was cascading around at the end of the last big ice age some 400,000 years ago. Nevertheless, it is these layers that stack up today to form the overall shape of the landscape. In other words we are thinking here of natural strata comprising Cretaceous, Pleistocene and Recent rocks.[1]

## A bird's eye view

Bizarrely, one starting point for understanding Norwich geology is to see it from the air. This may not be an obvious place to look from first, but it does help you to get a feel for the shape of the landscape in three dimensions. It enables you to see that much of the city centre nestles in a valley that is quite a lot lower-lying than the ground all around it.

In Figure 12 you can see the winding River Wensum, which has fallen a vertical height of more than 30 metres since it left Fakenham some 50 km back upstream. Although the river still has almost the same distance again to flow before it finally reaches the sea, it will hardly manage another metre fall all the way to Great Yarmouth. So the lowest parts of Norwich are not much above sea level. The daily tide gets up here; in fact the city lies at the head of the Yare estuary, with the present geological shoreline arguably at Acle. We shall look further at drainage in Chapter 3.

In recent years any aerial view would have showed the odd bare patch of subsoil exposed on city sites being made ready for construction – and there have been quite a few of those over the past few decades.

The colour of the exposed soil can vary a lot in different parts of the city, and that is all to do with which layer of natural strata is being dug up. For example, when the Chapelfield shopping centre was first excavated in 2003, there was a large blob of orange soil visible from above (in the bottom-right-hand section of Figure 12). A decade earlier in 1991 when Castle Mall was excavated, the scar there was mostly white. And on the lower-lying land between the railway station and the football ground, the Riverside development in 1998 was responsible for a wide area of dark brown, almost black soil.

---

1   Please don't be put off by this early slippage into use of geological terms. This account is not a course on geology, but a little groundwork is useful to help build our rational model. If you would like some more detailed treatment of local geology, publications on that subject are listed in the Further Reading section. These accounts inevitably have recourse to various special terms and Latin words that have always been part of the labelling used by learned geologists, but I am hoping such language can largely be avoided in this book. And whether the strata of the Norwich area can truly be described as 'rock' is debatable. I have rarely had cause to wield a hammer or pick in East Anglia, and my career as a 'soft rock' geologist has occasionally been a source of amusement to my more craggy geological colleagues working elsewhere.

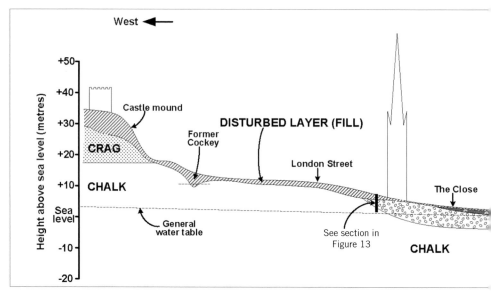

*Figure 14* Diagrammatic cross-section through Norwich city centre (not to scale)

## Different colours, different soil types

Of course, these various colours result from the natural soil types occurring in different places and at different levels in the ground.

While the geological layering in our part of the world is less complicated than elsewhere in the United Kingdom, it is not quite a simple matter of the soils being sandwiched in regular horizontal layers which were sliced through later by the Wensum valley. Thanks to an ice age or two and water flow cutting down in places in the past, some of the soil boundaries wander up and down as you follow them, in a less than predictable fashion. This is especially true of the underside of the layers of soil laid down by melting ice sheets, particularly if these rest directly on chalk.

The eroded upper surface of the chalk is the oldest geological stratum we are likely to encounter, and by the principle of superposition is at the bottom of the sequence (see the cross-section, Figure 14). In fact, you will find it eventually beneath all the later-deposited layers of soil wherever you are in the city and surrounding area (visible in Figure 13), and it extends to a depth considerably greater than you are ever likely to dig.

Norfolk Museums hold a splendid nineteenth-century painting by Frederick Bacon Barwell showing the original cattle market (held where the park above Castle Mall now is) looking down Rose Lane (Figure 15). In the background of the painting, dating from the 1870s, you can see the Thorpe hillside: that is, the rising ground on the opposite side of the river from Pull's Ferry. Unlike today, it was all white. That's because it was effectively one huge **chalk** quarry with a worked face rising 20 metres or more up the valley side. As we have already noted, the chalk underlies all parts of the city to a great depth, and it is a whole lot older than any of the other soils we find round here. The chalk was formed more than 70 million years ago at a time when our bit of continental crust lay much closer to the Equator than now (thanks to

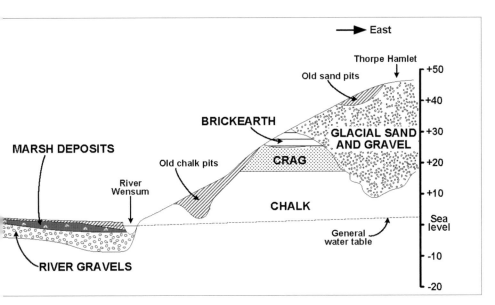

continental drift) and we sat somewhere within a wide tropical sea populated by countless billions of microscopic creatures, the accumulation of whose tiny shells over millions of years is what made the chalk.

Only a modest cannon shot away, in the area between Pull's Ferry and the Cathedral, the top of the chalk plunges away (or more accurately is eroded away) to 10 metres or more below river level, being replaced by a thick bed of brown **gravel** laid down within the last few tens of thousands of years by a faster-flowing version of the present River

*Figure 15 The Hill at Norwich on Market Day,* by Frederick Bacon Barwell, 1871

*Figure 16* Installation of piled foundations through peaty ground at Riverside, 1998, with Thorpe Railway Station in the background

Wensum as it snaked across the flood plain.

Once things had calmed down a bit and the weather had warmed up in pre-historic times, the valley floor became taken over by water-loving vegetation. On the inside of the river bends, a layer of black squelchy peat sits above the saturated gravel, and for most of the history of Norwich this soggy ground was only really of use for summer grazing for cattle on wide marshlands next to the river. The peaty content also explains the dark colour of the soil as exposed on the Riverside site a little further downstream between the railway station and Carrow Road, when it was originally built on in the 1930s and subsequently redeveloped in the 1990s (Figure 16).

Up on the higher ground away from the river, things are generally drier and also tend to be a bit more orange in colour, thanks to the natural sands that cover the chalk. These are known as the **crag**. These silty sands originally accumulated at the edges of an ancient sea (albeit nothing like as old as the chalk, only a mere 1–2 million years), and they were subsequently uplifted by earth movements to well above present sea level. The crag was the bright orange soil being dug out when the underground car parks of The Forum and Chapelfield sites were being excavated (Figure 17). At the deepest point, these holes were just about getting down to the underlying white chalk.

*Figure 17* Composite view of Chapelfield site from Malthouse Car Park, shortly before its demolition, April 2003

*Figure 18* Coarse gravels dropped originally by glacial meltwater forming higher ground at Beech Drive, Mousehold Heath

Then in the outskirts of the city centre and beyond is a highly variable covering of brown **glacial sand and gravel**, originally thrown down by melting ice water rushing around towards the end of the last ice age (Figure 18). This now tends to form the highest ground such as Mousehold, Thorpe and also the ridge now followed by Ber Street. Sometimes this stony layer sits above the crag and sometimes directly on the chalk without any crag being present in the sequence, probably because it was washed away by earlier meltwater.

For completeness, we must mention one or two other soil types that are important locally. These include **brickearth**, a brown sandy clay occurring for example in the Catton/Sprowston area – the name indicates what that was used for. It's a rather stickier soil than the sands generally found elsewhere (Figure 19). We also have, in a few places in the city, a firm light grey chalky clay called **till** or **boulder clay** – there's an isolated patch of that a few hundred metres across beneath the Hewett School playing field at

*Figure 19* Exposure of sandy clay (brickearth) at a redevelopment site at Union Street, June 2007

Lakenham, and a lot more of it forming the countryside southward from Norwich. Both of these mixed-up soil types are thought to have been dumped out of huge ice sheets.

There are also some very localised deposits called **head** in places on the steeper slopes, formed where water or semi-frozen ground has picked up soil and carried it farther down, either gradually or all in a rush, in a higgledy-piggledy heap sometimes called 'hill-wash'.

Plenty has been written by experts about the composition and occurrence of these various natural soil layers in the Norwich area; if you want to find out more, see 'Further Reading'. It is fascinating what can be deduced about past environments, and how these layers compare, and also contrast, with the geology of areas farther afield.

## The layer on the top

For many people the most interesting soil type in Norwich is the one at the top of the sequence, and (by the principle of superposition) the most geologically recent. It is the layer disturbed by humans' busy activities over the past couple of thousand years – and thus the layer of interest to historians, but we geologists and engineers usually call it **fill**.

Across most of the city centre is a blanket of dark-coloured fill typically extending between about 1 and 3 metres beneath our feet (Figure 20). It contains all the drains and buried cables we rely on, old foundations and rubble from countless demolished buildings, waste pits from ancient industrial processes, river dredgings, miscellaneous bits of

pottery and bones, and a fair amount of medieval dung. Archaeologists just love it.

The older layers of fill are of particular fascination because they combine the record of ongoing natural processes with the influence of activity by people not unlike us from however long ago. At these lower levels, where present, it is often difficult to draw a clear boundary between the human-influenced layers of soil and those of purely natural origin. This may be more a problem of the definitions we are using.

Since fill is not (by definition) a natural soil, we shall leave aside discussion of this layer for the moment, and return to it in Part II.

*Figure 20* Buried services, disturbed soil, Princes Street

# 3
# Terrain

Next in this first part of the book, continuing to look at Norwich's natural setting, we shall consider the shape of land surface that is effectively draped over the stack of soils previously discussed. We look at the ups and the downs, or the gradients, which of course have consequences for how water flows over that surface after it has fallen out of the sky – as it has always done with greater or lesser frequency.

## The shape of the city

Some people unfamiliar with the city may place rather too much reliance on Noel Coward's famous quote 'Very flat, Norfolk', uttered by Amanda in *Private Lives* (1930). Those who have been here know this is not at all an accurate description of Norwich. While Brian Ayers has described Norwich as 'one of the more hilly cities of lowland England',[2] William Smith commended Norwich streets being 'not like many in London and Manchester, uninterestingly level, or like Bath or Bristol, unpleasantly hilly'.[3]

We can get a feel for natural topography from a remarkable early aerial photograph (Figure 21) dating from 1897, some six years before the Wright Brothers flew for the first time. It was taken from a hot air balloon floating 100 metres or so above the castle, and the view is over Thorpe Railway Station and beyond along the curving and widening river valley, as the Wensum turns towards Yarmouth, with the ground rising on the Thorpe and Trowse sides.

*Figure 21* Eastward view towards Thorpe Station and beyond, from above the Cattle Market, 1897

2   *Norwich: Archaeology of a Fine City*, p. 18.
3   Untitled work on Norfolk, 1807.

Figure 22 Bishop's Bridge, by John Sell Cotman, c.1807

Figure 23 View from St Leonard's Road, 1985

Painters of the nineteenth-century Norwich School of Artists generally liked their landscapes, and they were adept at representing Norwich terrain in the background of their views of local landmarks – such as Bishop Bridge (Figure 22). Sometimes this 'alpine' scenery may seem to be an exaggeration made for artistic reasons, but in many cases it is an accurate representation of topography that may subsequently have been subdued by quarrying activities or later tree growth.

Horizontal telephoto views from ground level in the higher parts of the city, such as the Thorpe hillside

*Figure 24* Gas Hill, Norwich

*Figure 25* The author (right) participating in the Gas Hill Gasp, 2013

(Figure 23), can also give a good impression of how hilly parts of the city are. Look at the perspective lines made by the roofs or gutters of buildings not facing you square on. The apparent angle they make to the horizontal can tell you whether they are at a level above or below the camera's level. If they look horizontal, they are the same elevation as the photographer.

The steepest road in the city is undoubtedly Gas Hill. A longstanding Norwich tradition is an annual cycle race up this hill, which averages a gradient of 1 in 8 over its 250 metre length, but steepens viciously to 1 in 5.5 towards the top (Figures 24 and 25). The gasping cyclist reaching the summit will have the satisfaction of knowing they have ascended some 34 vertical metres from Riverside Road. I discuss whether the gradient itself is entirely natural in Part II, but there is no denying that the vertical elevation is the product of the natural geology in this part of the city.

It is possible to create a topographic map (Figure 26) that uses shading to emphasise the sloping sides to the river valley, contrasting these slopes with the plateau-like areas on higher ground and the flat valley floor each side of the River Wensum as it flows through the city centre.

The River Yare skirts round the south of Norwich before connecting with the River

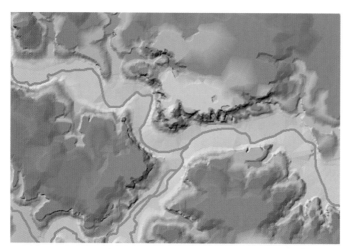

*Figure 26*
Topographic map
with 'relief'

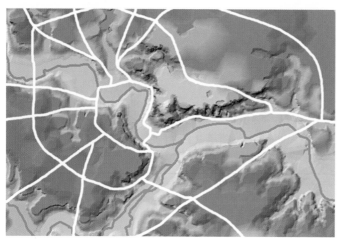

*Figure 27*
Map with road layout
superimposed

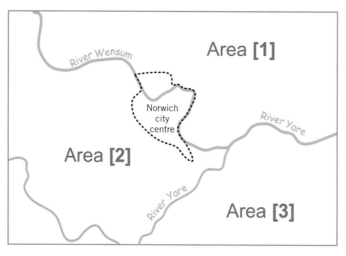

*Figure 28*
Rivers subdividing
Greater Norwich into
three areas

Tas, then joining the Wensum downstream of the city on its eastern side.[4] If we superimpose the modern road system (Figure 27), we can see how Greater Norwich is effectively subdivided by the river system into three main areas of higher ground:

1  to the north of the Wensum (from Hellesdon across to Mousehold and Thorpe St Andrew)
2  south of the Wensum and west of the Yare (Earlham through to Lakenham)
3  south of the Wensum and east of the Yare (Arminghall and Trowse).

These are shown on Figure 28.

There are also some other minor tributary valleys (visible on the topographic map) as we shall see again later.

So it is the flow of water cutting down into the landscape over the past few tens of thousands of years that is the main reason for Norwich being the physical shape it is. The River Wensum flowing through the centre of Norwich shows many of the classic features of a mature river, occupying a low-lying flood plain typically 200 to 400 metres wide, and meandering from one side of the low-lying area to the other.

Where the river gets close to the edge of the flood plain, it tends to nibble into the valley side. Thus the ground tends to rise steeply on the outside of the river bends as the consequence of geologically recent erosion, as can for example be seen in the Charing Cross, Kett's Hill and Carrow Hill areas of the city. On the inside of the meanders there

Figure 29 View across city centre from St Michael's Terrace, near the top of Gas Hill

---

4  Quite why the combined watercourse is called the Yare rather than the Wensum is a mystery: perhaps it is because 'Great Wensumouth' would be a bit of a mouthful.

are (or were) wide expanses of low marshy ground, such as at Coslany, Bishopgate and Carrow Road.

If our exhausted cyclist at the top of Gas Hill looks back over their shoulder, there is a spectacular view up the Wensum valley eastwards, over the Anglican Cathedral to St John's Roman Catholic Cathedral beyond (Figure 29).

And if we go a little farther round the hillside (beyond Kett's Hill and Gurney Road) to Mousehold Avenue, there is an equally impressive elevated view across the city centre, this time straight across the valley beyond the Cathedral on the lower ground to the Castle on the far side of the valley, with the Roman Catholic Cathedral this time off to the right. You get a good impression of how the oldest parts of the city centre nestle in the valley. Many of the medieval church towers are visible from here, still proudly poking up above the other city centre buildings, and our foreshortened telephoto view again helps us to appreciate the vertical difference in levels as we cross from one side of the city centre to the other (Figure 30). This angle on the city has inspired artists for centuries, as well as the early map-makers and drawers of elevated views, or 'prospects'.

## Using relative levels

One of the church towers visible in our telephoto view is St George Colegate, situated on relatively low ground in the north part of the city centre, an area known as Norwich Over the Water or Norwich Ultra Aquam. Let's now consider how we can use the tower as a ground-level measuring device, not unlike a surveyor's tripod.

*Figure 30* Foreshortened south-westward view from Mousehold Avenue, to St Giles, St Lawrence, St George Colegate and St John's Cathedral

*Figure 31*
Eastward view along Colegate from the church tower of St George Colegate, May 2009

As with many of the flint towers, it is still possible (with the necessary permission) to climb up inside via a spiral staircase or a ladder, in this case up through the medieval bell frame and out onto the roof of the tower, taking care not to lean out too far over the low stone parapet. The parapet at St George is some 26 metres above the street level, and there are splendid views eastwards beyond the medieval Cathedral towards Mousehold (Figure 31) as well as southwards over the nearby River Wensum towards the Castle and market place.

Once again, by looking at the lines of perspective made by the horizontal elements of buildings, we can work out what lies at about the same vertical level as our eyeline, where these perspective lines form a flat horizon: it is evident that we are looking in the same horizontal plane as, say, the first-floor windows of City Hall (Figure 32). They are actually about 7 metres above ground level in St Giles, whereas we are 26 metres above ground level at Colegate. So that tells us that the ground must rise some 19 metres (26 minus 7) from Norwich Over the Water to the City Hall area. That helps me to understand why I always seem a little short of breath whenever I return that way on my bicycle.

In order to quantify vertical levels, surveyors usually adopt the convention of measuring levels as heights above an arbitrary datum level (or horizontal line) known as 'Ordnance Datum', and is the system used on all Ordnance Survey maps in the United Kingdom. This

*Figure 32* View over Duke Street to City Hall from the top of St George Colegate

chosen datum level is effectively at sea level – more precisely, it's a fixed point midway between average high and low tides at Newlyn in Cornwall that has been transferred right across the country. Any point or horizontal plane can be represented as a height in metres above Ordnance Datum, or 'm AOD' for short. It is also possible to measure the depths of features below Ordnance Datum, such as the level of the sea bed.

The more detailed Ordnance Survey maps have approximate 'spot levels' marked at various places, and occasionally the measured values for accurate 'bench marks', lines which are chiselled onto suitable walls (Figure 33) allowing surveyors to measure directly from them instead of going to Cornwall. This book adopts the convention of putting + and – signs in front of levels that are above and below OD respectively.

The large-scale Ordnance Survey map for Colegate shows a bench mark on the churchyard wall near the church tower (indicated as 'BM'), labelled as +3.83 m AOD. The mark is a little way up the wall, so we can be fairly confident that street level is, to the nearest metre, at +3 m AOD. We can now calculate the approximate level of our eye line when we are up the 26 m high church tower: we climbed 26 m up from +3 m AOD, so our eye level is +29 m AOD. If we were looking truly horizontally across at City Hall then this means the first floor windows there must also be at +29 m AOD. To find the ground level in St Giles, we subtract 7 metres to get back down to ground level outside City Hall, which gives +22 m AOD. We can check this by then consulting the relevant Ordnance Survey map. It is reassuring to find a bench mark at the base of the tower of City Hall with a recorded value of of +22.25 m AOD, which suggests our crude levelling method is sound (Figure 34).

What we have done is essentially what the original Ordnance Survey map-makers did with their tripods and levelling equipment, setting up horizontal sight lines at given levels above OD and stepping up and down so as to measure relative ground levels over great distances, eventually right across the country. When thinking about things subterranean, we can use the same system to determine where we are vertically, whether above or below OD. We do this because it is a more fundamental and reliable means of recording things than simply as depth below ground level – for ground level can change over the years, whereas OD levels remain fixed in space.

Of course, when it comes to measuring the levels of things that exist below the ground, the technique is usually to measure the surface level in metres AOD, then to subtract the depth measured on a tape or plumb-line dangled down an excavation, well or borehole.

*Figure 33* Bench mark on churchyard wall, St George's Plain

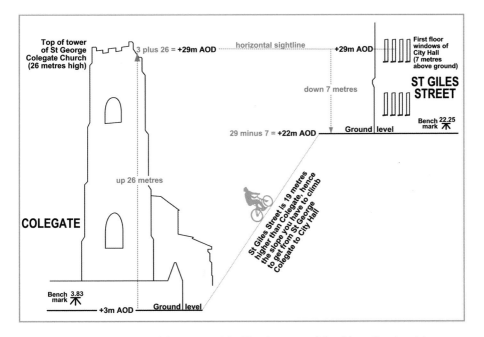

*Figure 34* The relative levels of Colegate and St Giles Street, as sighted from the church tower

## The higher parts of the city

Returning to the topographic map (Figure 27, page 22), we can see that City Hall is situated on the higher ground south of the River Wensum (the second area of high ground mentioned above). As you move farther out of the city centre and southwards across the residential area known as the Golden Triangle, the ground generally remains at an elevation of around +25 m AOD, give or take a few metres. Farther east, there is a small ridge along the line of Bracondale and Ber Street at up to about +35 m AOD, with the Castle mound forming its northernmost point. The bench mark outside the door to the Castle Museum has a value of +33.53 m AOD.

This is at a lesser elevation than the highest land north of the Wensum (area 1 in Figure 28, page 22), which climbs up to about +50 m AOD in the area of the white water tower in Quebec Road, Thorpe Hamlet, not far from the top of Gas Hill (Figure 35). In fact there is a bench mark on the north-west side of the water tower with the value of +50.10 m AOD.

The very highest land in the Norwich area is reached in the third area lying south of the Wensum and east of the Yare (area 3). The surface rises progressively from Trowse and Arminghall southward to Poringland, where it reaches a dizzy +75 m AOD in the vicinity of the two large radio masts (Figure 36). That is why they are positioned there, as was a nearby Second World War anti-aircraft battery, the remains of which can still be seen off Chandler Road, Upper Stoke Holy Cross.

*Figure 35* Eastward view towards St Michael's Terrace on Gas Hill from the tower of St Lawrence's Church, showing the water tower at Quebec Road

*Figure 36* Radio masts on high ground at Upper Stoke Holy Cross, near Poringland

## The lowest parts of the city

Not surprisingly, the lowest land is generally next to the river. We have already seen that road level in Colegate in Norwich Over the Water is at only about +3 m AOD. Farther downstream each side of the Wensum, parts of Bishopgate and Barrack Street are at barely +2 m AOD, and some of the land adjacent to Norwich City Football Club's stadium at Carrow Road is (or at least was) even lower.

## Water levels

Given that OD level is roughly the same as average sea level (in other words, the typical tidal range is each side of zero OD), it is no surprise that the lowest parts of the city (Figure 37) have from time to time been subject to flooding following temporary rises in river level. However the worst flooding in Norwich has actually resulted from river water coming down the river from the higher ground of central Norfolk, rather than from seawater travelling up the river from Great Yarmouth.

The most severe event in recent history was the flooding of August 1912, which followed a prolonged period of torrential summer rainfall. The highest water levels reached are recorded by several flood plates on river walls and nearby buildings around the city, and it is a relatively straightforward thing to measure the levels of these local flood levels in metres AOD.

The water level in the river on the downstream side of the weir at New Mills (Figure 38) is typically around +1 m AOD,[5] whereas on the upstream side the water is usually held (by a control sluice) at a level between +2 and +3 m AOD. During the 1912 flood the swollen river rose to above +4 m AOD behind this constriction, explaining the

---

5  This level is in any case subject to tidal fluctuation because of the influence of the sea at Great Yarmouth. Normally this fluctuation at Norwich occurs over considerably less than 1 metre.

*Figure 37* The River Wensum in the heart of Norwich (St George's Bridge)

*Figure 38* New Mills, viewed from the downstream side

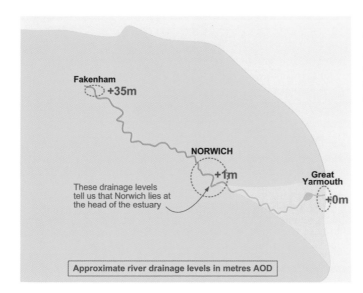

*Figure 39*
Approximate river
levels in the River
Wensum and Lower
Yare showing how
most of the fall
occurs upstream of
Norwich (sketch map,
not to scale)

overspilling that took place in the Heigham Street and Barn Road areas where the ground level is itself only around +3 m AOD. Further downstream the flooding took place at a lower relative level. I look in more detail at the causes of flooding in Part II of this book (Chapter 10).

Standing back and looking at Norwich in a more regional context, it is interesting to look at how the relative level of the mighty River Wensum falls along its course from west Norfolk. It starts as a small stream near the village of Whissonsett on ground at a level of about +50 m AOD and runs for some 13 km before it reaches Fakenham Mill. At this point the river water level is at just over +34 m AOD, which level if transferred straight to Norwich would put the river some 5 m higher than the top of the church tower at Colegate, and not far below the roof of City Hall. It is just as well that the River Wensum flows downhill between Fakenham and Norwich, or we would all be below the waterline.

From Fakenham to Norwich the winding River Wensum falls vertically some 33 m over a river distance of 61 km, an average gradient of about 1 in 1,850. In reality, much of the fall occurs in incremental steps as the river drops peacefully over the eleven weirs or mill runs along the way. This upper course of the river is actually a raging torrent compared with its sluggish progress the 50 km from the lower side of New Mills all the way to Great Yarmouth, over which the total vertical fall is no more than a fraction of 1 m, and the river is daily subject to reversed tidal flow.

What this profile tells us is that Norwich is effectively at the head of the Yare estuary, which explains why the valley quickly opens out to a width of several hundred metres as soon as you get downstream of Carrow and Trowse (Figure 39). Until construction of the A47 road viaduct at Postwick in 1992, there were historically no fixed river crossings all the way from Carrow until you reached Great Yarmouth, and it remains the case that Reedham Ferry is the only way to get across if you don't have access to a boat.

## Soil boundary levels

We can use exactly the same method of levelling to position soil layers vertically in relation to their height above or below OD (approximate sea level). Most layers of soil have an upper and lower boundary, in other words the top and bottom of the layer at any given location. We will ideally want to determine the level of these boundaries in relation to OD, rather than just the depth below the present ground surface.

Tripod surveying techniques can be used to measure directly the levels of soil exposed in a trench or quarry. If on the other hand the soils are down a borehole, we can measure the ground level at the top of the borehole in metres AOD, then simply subtract from this the measured depth down the hole to the boundary we are interested in to get its relative level.

By thinking of relative levels (rather than just depths) we have a powerful way of fixing soil boundary levels in space, rather than just recording a depth below a ground surface that might subsequently be raised or lowered. It also enables us to compare and predict the positions of equivalent soil layers in different parts of the city and beyond.

Some soil boundary levels are reasonably consistent and horizontal across the Norwich area, making it straightforward to predict where we can expect to find them in relation to a given ground level. An example is the boundary between the crag and underlying chalk (Figure 40), which is often found to occur at a level of around +15 to +18 m AOD. The reason is that the crag was originally laid down on a roughly level surface cut by the sea.

Other boundary levels are more difficult to predict because they vary a lot over short horizontal distances. This is usually because of the way the soils were deposited. An example is the underside of the glacial sand and gravel, which may be steeply inclined across any particular site, perhaps found resting on crag in one place and on chalk at a lower level in another part of the site. This can be explained by the erosion of steep localised valley features by glacial meltwater prior to the accumulation of the sand and gravel.

*Figure 40* Boundary between the chalk and overlying Norwich crag, as exposed in St James' Pit off Gurney Road

# 4
# Surface drainage

As we know, rain (or its frozen equivalent) falls from the sky frequently, and where this water goes when it strikes the ground depends very much on the steepness and direction of slope, and on what the ground is made of – in other words, on the topography and the geology.

In the case of a developed city, the nature of the surfacing (whether hard-paved or otherwise) and the provision of drain gullies (and their maintained condition) are crucially important in where the water goes next.

In the natural situation, a layer of topsoil will soak up an initial accumulation of water, but sooner or later the water might start to flow laterally across the surface, when it will usually take the steepest course. Thus the surface water becomes concentrated into a local streamlet which may in time erode its own course down the slope. You can still see this process happening in some parts of the city (Figure 41).

Because much of the natural geology in Norwich is relatively open-textured (and therefore allows water to soak in), there is not an extensive visible network of tributary streams feeding into the Rivers Wensum or Yare. However there is evidence for a number of former watercourses, and valleys that have served to drain the landscape at some time in the past. Some of these streams are known to have been flowing in historical times; others may be relics from an earlier but geologically recent time when there was more meltwater and/or permafrost, and thus more water at the surface (Figure 42). Other apparent watercourses may be drainage pathways that only functioned during extreme weather conditions.

*Figure 41* Eroded mini stream bed forming in Lion Wood, off Wellesley Avenue North, Thorpe Hamlet

We can see these tributary valleys on the topographic map of the area (Figure 26). Within the city centre, we know of several lost watercourses from historical information such as old maps and place-names (I look at these specifically in Chapter 8). They often originate in locations where the shallow soil is less permeable than elsewhere, such as over brickearth or glacial till, where you would expect a tendency for rainfall to accumulate at the surface rather than soak straight into the ground.

Nowadays over much of the city centre there is a high percentage of 'hard cover', in the form of manufactured paving or the roofs of buildings, so the surface drainage is to a large extent the consequence of artificial provision. In most cases it means piping the collected water into drains and 'storm' sewers, which may or may not follow the approximate lines of earlier watercourses before they find their way to the river. Some of the water will inevitably get into the parallel system of 'foul' sewers and be taken straight to Whitlingham Sewage Treatment Works, while a certain proportion of the rainfall still manages to soak into the ground near to where it fell, as it has for centuries, adding to what we know as **groundwater**.

These days it is recognised that for environmental and sustainability reasons it is desirable for the groundwater 'reservoir' to be continuously topped up, hence the preference for piping roofwater into soakaways wherever possible, rather than sending it down drains discharging into the rivers which means most of the fresh water is eventually lost into the sea.

*Figure 42* A dry valley at St James' Hill off Britannia Road, formed after the last major glaciation about 400,000 years ago

# 5
# Groundwater

The rainwater that does sink into the ground, or gets there via local soakaways or leaking drain pipes, generally percolates downwards where the ground is free-draining enough, unless intercepted first by the root hairs of some nearby tree – in which case it could be sucked up and transpired back into the atmosphere as water vapour during summer drought conditions.

## Soil permeability

The movement of water through the ground is largely driven by gravity, and the speed at which it moves is a function of the soil's permeability (Figure 43), which in turn depends on the size of the soil particles. Where the soil is of low permeability, say brickearth or a particularly clayey layer in the chalk, the downward progress of the infiltrated water is impeded, and it will spread out, or pond, above the soil layer (in the form of 'perched water'). Continuing to move sideways, it may eventually find a route downwards past the less permeable layer or just dissipate slowly into the underlying soil.

In sloping parts of the city, especially where steep slopes have been artificially cut, the sideways movement of groundwater sometimes causes it to emerge again at the surface down-gradient from where it started, which results in a spring. There are one or two historical examples in the city (Figure 44).

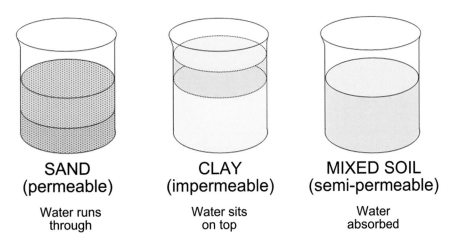

### SAND
### (permeable)
Water runs
through

### CLAY
### (impermeable)
Water sits
on top

### MIXED SOIL
### (semi-permeable)
Water
absorbed

*Figure 43* Idealised comparison of what happens when water is added to beakers containing soil with varying particle size profiles: from left to right, coarse soil, fine soil and an intermediate mixture (silty soil, or loam)

*Figure 44* A former spring near Bishop Bridge around 1834, engraved by C. Fox after a painting by James Stark. This would have become dangerously polluted later as it was directly downslope from the gas works.

## The water table

Leaving aside any localised perched water in the ground, it is important to realise that there is groundwater sitting beneath the whole of the city (and indeed county) in the form of saturated soil. This is present below a certain depth that is quite well understood and predictable in terms of its relative level (in m AOD). It is indicated on the schematic cross-section of the city centre (Figure 14, page 14).

This base 'water table' is closely related to the level in watercourses, so unsurprisingly the groundwater level near to the river will be similar to river level (allowing for a little short-term tidal fluctuation). In the heart of the city that will probably mean slightly below +1 m AOD, so it is easy to know how far down to expect the ground to be saturated if we already know the ground level. The groundwater level is likely to be about a metre or more higher than this beneath those areas adjacent to the river upstream of New Mills, because the river level is correspondingly higher.

As we move farther away from the river and up the valley sides, the level of the water table (expressed in metres AOD) tends to rise gradually, much less steeply than does the ground surface, by perhaps 2–3 m in the first kilometre, so beneath the inner suburbs of the city we can expect groundwater to be still below about +5 m AOD. On the south side of the city, the water table will at some stage be connected to the River Yare which falls from a level of about +8 m AOD in Bowthorpe to around +3 m AOD at Lakenham Mill. In Norfolk as a whole, the level of the base water table rises away from the coast, Broads and inland river valleys, to reach +40 m AOD (and in some cases higher) beneath the 'plateau' areas in the central parts of the county.

It is thus possible to plot a contoured map of the surface of the water table, and this generally looks rather like a milder version of the topographic map (Figure 45). The direction of groundwater flow at any point will always be the steepest downward slope on the surface of the water table (in other words, at right angles to the contours), and this is nearly always towards the nearest river.

## Measuring the standing water level

The most direct way of accurately measuring the groundwater level is to leave a deep excavation open overnight (appropriately fenced for safety, and with the sides supported if necessary) and to return in the morning. Sometimes water appears overnight in a temporary pit, either unintentionally (as is apparent in Figure 13, page 12), or where a small excavation is made for that purpose (Figure 46).

A more elegant and accurate method is to install a monitoring pipe in a borehole. In any kind of monitoring hole, time must be allowed for the equilibrium water level to be established, and this can be measured as a depth in metres below a known datum at ground level, and thus converted to a relative level in metres AOD.

By taking accurate measurements from three boreholes arranged in a triangle, we can work out the exact slope on the water table locally, and hence know the direction the groundwater is flowing. This is especially useful if there has been underground pollution,

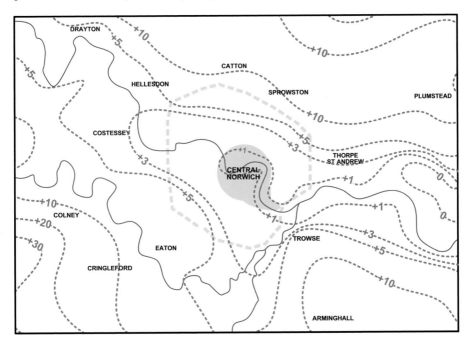

*Figure 45* Indicative contours on the water table in the Norwich area, expressed as metres above Ordnance Datum, based on published and unpublished local data. Contours are shown at zero, +1, +3, +5, +10, +20 and +30 m AOD.

*Figure 46* Archaeological excavations in December 2015 at Muspole Street revealed medieval quarry pits extending into the underlying natural terrace sand. One hole was taken deep enough to encounter the water table at around +1 m AOD.

and we want to know in which direction contaminants have been taken by the natural movement of groundwater.

The geology of Norwich does not really lend itself to the idea of discrete underground rivers, although this idea is attractive to some, especially water diviners with their dowsing rods. The fact is that a water well sunk anywhere in the city will encounter groundwater if it is taken below the base water table indicated. There will however be some variability in the rate at which water can be extracted from such a well, depending on the permeability of the soil around the section of well shaft within the saturated zone.

## Water bores

Major abstraction boreholes are usually taken down to well below the top of the water table and very deep into the chalk. For example, a borehole drilled in 1862 at Carrow Works was taken to a depth of 363 metres, more than 350 metres of which was through water-bearing chalk, before an underlying layer of sand then clay was encountered. The great depth was to provide a large area of interface between the borehole liner and the saturated soil to improve the yield of water when pumped, to access the more permeable chalk at depth, and hopefully to be able to take the water from below a level likely to be affected by pollution from the river or ground surface. There were many deep abstraction boreholes beneath the city centre (Figure 47).

*Figure 47* Archaeological dig on former Morgan's Brewery site, near St Julian's Alley, King Street in November 2000. The large vertical pipe sticking out of the ground is the casing of a former abstraction borehole.

*Figure 48* Initial excavation and piling for The Forum, viewed from Theatre Street, June 1999

# Part II

# Norwich resculpted

*Figure 49* View of the city from near the top of Gas Hill, engraving from a drawing of 1792, and the comparative view 220 years later

# 6
# A thousand years of activity

Norwich is not the oldest city in the kingdom, but it is ancient enough, and grew to become one of the foremost English cities for several centuries, with recurring periods of success and prosperity. This means that people have been busily engaged in intensive activity, both on and below the ground surface, for at least a thousand years. The effects of all this digging and delving can be profound – both in regard to the localised conditions we are left with on individual sites, and also in terms of the large-scale resculpting of swathes of the city in places (Figure 49).

## Modifications to the natural topography

In general, the effect on the urban landscape of continuous occupation is to 'smear out' the original topographic features, resulting in decreased slope angles and less prominent changes in ground level. This is probably true of any city, and is a normal process as generations of occupants seek to make the place more habitable over time. Perhaps the most obvious example is the infilling of the stream courses that used to pass through the city centre, coupled with a typical slow building-up of the ground surface over the centuries.

Some activities can actually do the opposite: they enhance the topography, by increasing the original slope angles. For example this includes the creation of steep quarry faces in what were previously more gently sloping natural hillsides, and the deliberate creation of defensive fortifications such as ditches, banks and mounds designed to slow down potential attackers.

In many cases however, the effect of all those centuries of urban activity is to leave the original ground level largely unchanged, but nevertheless to create a hidden legacy whereby there is disturbance of the ground to some depth below the ground surface. This occurs through multiple phases of digging out and filling in – more often than not in an unplanned way. The original natural geological profile has been modified into something different.

We look below in more detail at the processes leading to raised ground and lowered ground, and the relationship between the two.

## The archaeological legacy

Almost all of the medieval city has been left mantled by a layer of disturbed soil which consists of an admixture of constituents varying continuously, both vertically and horizontally. It is often dark-coloured and is the uppermost layer encountered in any excavation. It was labelled 'fill' on the cross-section (Figure 14, page 14) because that is the name most commonly given to it, at least by geologists and construction engineers. Equivalent terms are 'filled ground', 'made ground' and 'disturbed ground', but if you are a historian you might equally refer to this as 'archaeology' (Figure 50).

It is characterised by its unpredictability, which is why archaeologists find it so interesting. It can tell us much about what was going on when it was put there, and often

*Figure 50* Archaeological excavation at the site of the Cathedral Hostry, 2007, showing the zone of medieval backfill against the wall line

contains preserved artefacts, such as telltale fragments of pottery or occasionally more complete items of the kind that are exhibited in museums.

The thickness of this layer can vary considerably in different parts of the city, and can also fluctuate significantly across any one site. A depth of 1–2 m is not uncommon in the city centre, but it can be much thicker, for example where bomb craters were filled in (Figure 51). Equally, there are some locations where there is little or no fill, and the undisturbed natural ground occurs very close to the present surface.

In the lowest-lying parts of the city nearest to the river, the deepest (and therefore the earliest) layers of disturbed ground consist in large degree of natural river mud, mixed with added soil, sunken brick/timber fragments or other human-made material from when the land was first reclaimed. In saturated ground, organic remains such as timber or leather can survive for centuries. Elsewhere in the city the oldest fill is usually dark coloured and largely made up of a mixture of what was originally topsoil, medieval dung and other degradable waste. As we come up the sequence into later (post-medieval) fill, the proportion of building detritus (lime, flint and brick fragments) tends to increase, and the most recent fill often consists of imported rubble, sand, buried rubbish or the compacted layers of crushed stone supporting the most recent paving or placed around pipes or cables.

Archaeologists get most excited (and engineers correspondingly spooked) when the underside of the fill suddenly slopes away along the edge of an exploratory trench to reveal some human-made feature such as a post-hole or a kiln. In many cases the reasons for

*Figure 51* Bomb crater, April 1942, at St Benedict's Gate: the view is along St Benedict's Street from the bottom of Grapes Hill

such 'random' fluctuations are not immediately apparent, and need careful interpretation. The most extreme depth variation occurs when an old filled well is exposed, potentially extending the zone of infill right down to a level below the water table, perhaps tens of metres below the surface.

Both engineers and archaeologists have reasons to be slightly obsessed about the likely depth of the disturbed zone on any site. For archaeologists it is useful to know in advance how wide they should start their trench, in order to dig down in comfortable stages (creating steps) to reach the top of the natural ground. For engineers, stable foundations usually need to be taken down through those variable dark-coloured layers into the undisturbed natural soil (usually orange-brown or white in Norwich), which is traditionally regarded as having more predictable bearing characteristics. Having an idea beforehand of the minimum excavation depth required to do this is again helpful, in planning the most economical foundation system.

*Figure 52* Retaining wall at St John Maddermarket, probably constructed
when the road was widened in 1578

# 7
# Raised ground

## Incidental raising of ground level

We noted above how there was a seemingly inexorable process of the ground surface rising over the centuries in many parts of the city. One illustration of this process is that many of the older buildings have their ground floor levels rather low in relation to present external levels, often necessitating the need to walk down one or two steps when entering the property from the street. It would appear that they were built at a time when the ground level was lower than it is today.

This is certainly true of most medieval churches, many of which are now below present street level. This can make them vulnerable to flash flooding should the road drain gullies become blocked. Furthermore, the steps down into the church present a challenge in providing access for disabled people without having to construct unsightly access ramps.

Churchyards are in any case often very high in relation to the ancient buildings they surround as the direct result of their use for multiple burials over the centuries (Figure 52). That they were getting over-full was recognised in the nineteenth century, and in 1855 an order was issued to cease burials in the city churches. Some decades later there was widespread clearance of gravestones from the churchyards to provide green spaces for the benefit of the cramped city centre population, with many of the stone slabs subsequently reused to pave pathways around the buildings or incorporated into retaining walls to support the raised ground level of the graveyard adjacent to the church, or along the site boundary.

More generally throughout the city, the ground level was gradually increasing with generations of rebuilding over the centuries, with a tendency for later buildings to be constructed over the demolished remains of the previous ones. This effect is often visible as layers of building detritus within the layer of fill exposed in exploratory trenches (Figure 53).

## Deliberate raising of ground level

We can identify plenty of places where the original ground level has been raised on purpose.

### For fortifications

The most obvious example of raised defensive earthworks in Norwich is the Norman Castle mound, but there were also earlier tenth-century (Anglo-Scandinavian) fortifications which consisted of a bank (and corresponding ditch) around a D-shaped enclosure on the north side of the River Wensum. The bank has long disappeared as a visibly raised feature, but the alignment of one side of the earthworks is preserved as the curve of St George's Street and Calvert Street, between which the remains of the bank (and ditch) were identified in an archaeological excavation in 1990.

*Figure 53*
Archaeological
inspection trench off
Pitt Street, 2010,
showing typical
layering of detritus
above the natural
sand strata

*Figure 54 (right)*
Early stages during
construction of Castle
Mall, June 1990:
view towards Farmer's
Avenue showing
large excavation
intersecting the
Barbican ditch, visible
as darker coloured soil

The later Castle earthworks constructed by the Normans following their arrival in the late eleventh century were on an altogether larger scale, and involved significant raising of ground level in places using the soil dug out of adjacent defensive ditches. This major resculpting must have created a most impressive and impregnable-looking landscape (which was the whole idea), but one which was probably subject to ongoing erosion and degradation. This meant there was a need for regular work to maintain the slopes and the full height of the banks. In later years when there was less need for such defences there must have been progressive decay and 'smearing out', but most of the remaining vertical impact was eliminated deliberately when the outer defences were largely levelled in the eighteenth and nineteenth centuries to create usable open space for the cattle market. In recent years the ground level has gone upward again following the insertion of a subterranean shopping mall with its somewhat elevated rooftop garden (Figure 54).

Much of this completely resculpted area is likely to be at a higher elevation now than before the Normans arrived, and even the remaining defensive ditches of the Castle Gardens have been partly infilled and are thus arguably areas of raised ground. The dramatic castle mound still dominates its surroundings, but not all of its apparent height and bulk is

necessarily raised ground. The castle keep was deliberately constructed on a natural hill (Figure 55) which forms the northern end of the ridge along which Ber Street runs (at around +30 m AOD). The mound was enhanced by the Normans by digging out the intervening space to cut it off from the rest of the ridge, in the area now occupied by the roof of Castle Mall.

*Figure 55* The castle lift shaft under construction in 2001: some of the excavation through the mound may be into undisturbed natural ground

*Figure 56* Present-day flood plain in a rural setting near Ashwellthorpe, Norfolk

## On flood plains

Urban settlements need ready access to the river for both water and transport, and the early settlers were undoubtedly inconvenienced by having to tread onto low-lying squelchy land along the river margins. The situation is potentially least problematic if the meandering river is at one side of its flood plain and thus close to the adjacent rising (and drier) ground. This helps to explain where the earliest settlements were located, such as in the area between Tombland and Quayside. However, in most parts of the city centre the Wensum was flanked on both sides by low-lying marshy flood plains (Figure 56). There is evidence from archaeological excavations (such as at Fishergate) that attempts were made to stabilise the muddy surface in Anglo-Scandinavian times by placing a lattice of brushwood to make it easier to cross on foot and to allow small boats to be drawn up out of the water on a gentle ramp (Figure 57).

*Figure 58* Composite semi-panoramic photograph of Duke's Palace Wharf site prior to construction of a multi-storey car park and flats: ground investigation borehole in progress, April 2003

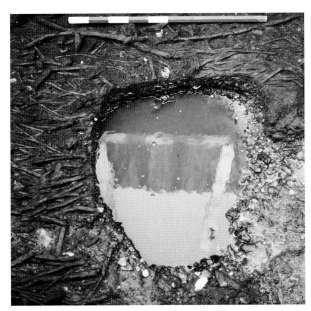

*Figure 57* Brushwood surface c.1,000 years old exposed at 4 m below ground level in an archaeological trench at Fishergate in 1979

As activities continued and the town developed, it was only a matter of time before posts and planks were driven in at appropriate places to separate the water from the mud, followed by scraping of the bed and filling behind the heading with dredged material to build up the level of the mooring at the river edge. Later improvements which we know were already well advanced in some places by the eleventh and twelfth centuries include the construction of long timber quays (such as at Quayside) with extensive ground-raising by infilling behind, using a combination of mud dredged from the river and sand/gravel scraped from further up the slope.

And so we can discern a typical development process along the edges of the river at various times in many parts of the city, which has led to canalisation of the watercourse and the progressive accumulation in many places of a wedge of filled ground, as much as 3–4 m thick on the river frontage, then tapering away from the river back to the original edge of the flood plain (Figures 58 and 59).

The street pattern often gives us a clue to where the edge of the marshy area was, because that is more often than not the position of ancient roadways that follow river valleys – along the lowest possible path not subject to regular flooding or instability. This may explain the

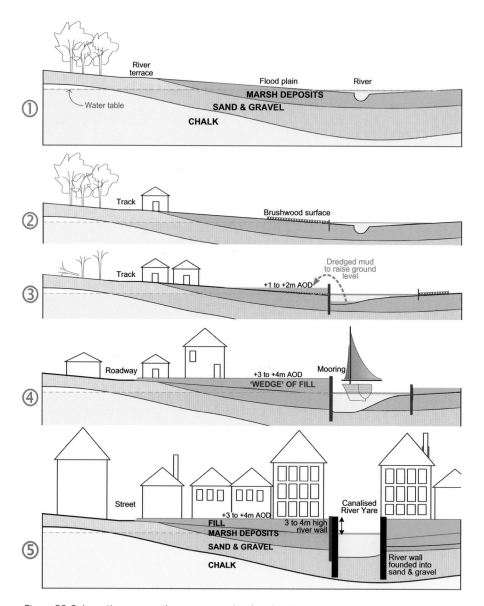

*Figure 59* Schematic cross-section sequence showing development over historical time of a typical 'wedge of fill' over former flood plain areas associated with canalisation of rivers

subtle curves of some Norwich streets which run roughly parallel to the river and were originally adjacent to the squelchy flood plain. Examples of former flood plains are Colegate southwards, Fishergate southwards, Barrack Street southwards (Figure 60) and the lower part of King Street eastwards.

Today such roads may lie some distance from the present river channel, but it is a fair bet that the present ground profiles will differ on opposite sides of the road. On the side

*Figure 60* Installation of the piled foundations of the Jarrold Bridge south of Barrack Street, Summer 2011, to carry the load below the fill and soft river deposits

away from the river we can expect to find natural dry soil at a relatively shallow depth, whereas on the other side the flat surface may mask an increasing thickness of built-up soil (fill) as you go towards the river. The lower levels of this wedge of fill may be admixed with (or resting on) natural river deposits, which are frequently found to be soft and water-bearing even before any underlying permeable river gravel is encountered.

Other roadways run at right angles to the river, aligned on the approach to ancient river crossings or watering points. Where these had to cross a considerable width of flood plain, they are likely to have originally been on a raised causeway (such as at Bishopgate, Fye Bridge Street or the much later Prince of Wales Road), with the ground level originally falling away on each side of the road. In many cases the adjacent land was later gradually raised (and so reclaimed) by further filling over the flood plain, for example at St George's Street.

In the 1980s a new gable wall was constructed on the site of a former shoe factory at St George's Street in Norwich Over the Water not far from St George's Bridge (Figure 61). The construction engineer was not local and evidently did not appreciate he would be digging through the wedge of fill towards its thicker end. A foundation trench was dug down through a considerable thickness of unstable dark-coloured soil, finally scrunching into water-bearing sand and gravel at a depth in excess of 4 m. An attempt to place a concrete footing in the base of this trench was abandoned when the sides fell in, and the extension

*Figure 61* The Atrium building, off St George's Street

was eventually constructed on deep-piled foundations.

## Over stream courses

We noted above how central Norwich was previously crossed by several watercourses forming side tributaries to the Wensum, and it is only recently that the local topographical significance of these has been fully appreciated. I look in more detail at the routes of these streams in Chapter 9, but here we can note how the local infilling of stream courses is another form of ground-raising, and one which can result in the local surface level rising by a surprising amount (several metres) owing to the depth of the original valley feature.

The most well-known stream course through the city centre was of the Great Cockey, running generally northwards en route to the Wensum from the west side of the Ber Street ridge. This crossed what is now Davey Place close to its junction with Castle Street. Some ground investigation in 1997 in the basement of the adjacent Castle House (which fronts onto Castle Meadow) was taken down into the natural chalk, and this traced what appeared to be the buried profile of the east side of the Cockey valley falling towards the Castle Street frontage, where a lowest level of +9 m AOD was recorded just off the line of the stream (Figure 62). The present ground surface at Davey Place is at +15 m AOD, which suggests that the infill was in excess of 6 m deep at this point. It seems the original stream ran (probably intermittently) in something of a ravine, a deep valley across which the castle garrison watched over the medieval market place on the opposite side. It is easy to see how this valley would quickly have become a place for accumulation of rubbish or spoil, and was progressively filled and then covered over. It is now the course of a drainage culvert.

Little more than 200 m downstream further north, the line of the Great Cockey crossed Bedford Street, and in 1991 its valley was identified in exploratory boreholes to the rear of the telephone exchange fronting St Andrew's Street. Here the apparent infill was observed extending down to just below +1 m AOD at the deepest point, which may be compared with the existing surface levels of +10 m AOD in Bedford Street and almost +6 m AOD in St Andrew's Street. Here too the stream seems to have run in a fairly steep-sided valley or gully, probably broadening towards the former Wensum flood plain on the north side of St Andrew's Street. It is possible that the watercourse was originally crossed here by some sort of causeway or bridge structure, the remains of which it is thought could still be buried below the street among the pipes and service ducts.

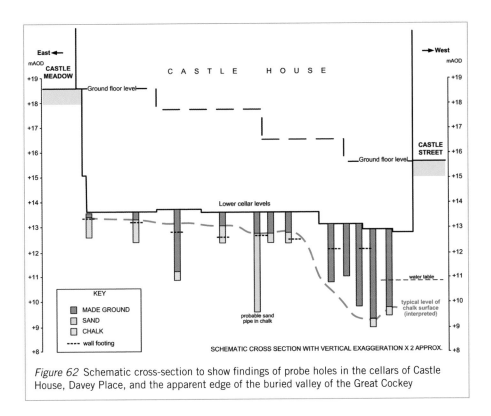

*Figure 62* Schematic cross-section to show findings of probe holes in the cellars of Castle House, Davey Place, and the apparent edge of the buried valley of the Great Cockey

## For access ramps

In some parts of the city very steep slopes have been created either by natural processes (such as river erosion) or more commonly by quarrying activities or building clearance. A steep slope or cliff can be a significant impediment to urban movement, and so there are examples where ramps of soil have been constructed to reduce the gradient, thus locally raising the ground level.

Early examples probably exist in the vicinity of the Castle and Rose Lane area, but these are difficult to untangle from later earthworks. Elsewhere, it is uncertain at present whether Gas Hill follows a natural slope profile or is constructed on a ramp of soil up a quarried hillside (see the background of Figure 15, page 15). More recently, the Victorians were not averse to the construction of earth ramps for new roads, such as at the top of Prince of Wales Road (1860), for the terraced houses built on Knowsley Road off Magdalen Road (circa 1888), and the link for trams between St Andrew's Street and Redwell Street (1899). When St Peter's Street was demolished in 1935 ahead of the construction of City Hall, the road was widened and slightly realigned westwards (Figure 63). The ground level was raised by up to 1.5 m to create a roughly level space in front of the building and a storage bunker beneath the adjacent memorial gardens. Construction of the wide inner ring road in 1969–71 required a ramped approach to the Magdalen Street flyover and some slightly incongruous road connections forced across the natural gradient, at locations such as Cleveland Road.

*Figure 63* St Peter's Street, viewed from Labour in Vain Yard, in the 1890s (left) and in 2010

## Old spoil heaps

We look more systematically at quarrying for resources in the next chapter, but it is worth noting here that almost all holes dug to extract useful construction materials also produce significant quantities of spoil – that is, surplus or unusable material. An example is the sand layer overlying the chalk that is waiting to be extracted. This spoil has to be placed somewhere, perhaps only temporarily, even if it ultimately becomes backfill to the quarry in question.

The bulky nature of old quarry spoil and the general lack of much admixed topsoil or human detritus mean that it is often difficult to identify when uncovered later in urban situations, because it can look much the same as the natural soils that would be expected in the vicinity. Sometimes the most telling way of distinguishing bulk fill from in situ natural soil is to measure its state of compaction, because the fill is generally looser than its undisturbed natural equivalent. That requires some means of measuring relative density, such as ground probing or penetration tests.

A proportion of the orange sand overburden originally shifted to get at the chalk in the hillside above Rosary Road was evidently dragged across to backfill earlier workings in the Chalk Hill House area, leaving a thick mantle of variably chalky (but natural-looking) sand extending across a previously worked area of uncertain form (Figure 64).

Similarly, the former chalk quarries in the area outside St Giles Gate to the north of Earlham Road (West Pottergate area) seem to have been backfilled with predominantly sand spoil perhaps originating from temporary spoil heaps along Earlham Road. There is a record from 1578 of the preparation for Queen Elizabeth I's visit to Norwich which (among other things) involved 'the narrow way at St Giles's Gate being enlarged by casting down the hills', which could be a reference to the disposal of spoil heaps which had accumulated from quarrying that we know was in progress nearby at around that time. In this case it is possible the spoil was pushed into old pits farther down the slope (Figure 65). When the site next to the top of Grapes Hill was excavated in preparation for a development of retirement housing, a considerable depth of disturbed sandy soil was indeed encountered (visible in Figure 145 on page 124).

In the 1940s and early 1950s, extensive clearance of wartime bombsites in central Norwich generated large quantities of soil, rubble and ash needing to be quickly cleared away to allow the roads to reopen, houses to be repaired where possible or the placement of prefabricated homes. Much of this was carted to the Mile Cross area and tipped onto the Wensum floodplain to create the raised ground of Anderson's Meadow and the industrial land in the Swanton Road area. The westernmost edge of the zone of tipped spoil is still visible as a steep bank near to Sloughbottom Park, with the unaffected area of Sweetbriar Marshes lying beyond (Figure 66).

Figure 64 Composite view of excavation in 1989 in front of Chalk Hill House, off Rosary Road, showing bulk quarry spoil in situ

*Figure 65* Extract from William Cunningham's prospect of Norwich of 1558, representing Earlham Road to the right of the figures and the slope down to Dereham Road to the left

*Figure 66* The edge of the filled ground at Sweetbriar Marshes, viewed from Marriott's Way near Sloughbottom Park

# 8
# Lowered ground

## Localised lowering of ground

At some places in the city we can see that the original ground has been dug away and the surface lowered for a specific purpose. A clear example is the former railway cutting now occupied by Lakenham Way (Figure 67). This was gouged out in 1848 in order to create a 'permanent way' at the intended level for trains running into the former Victoria Station at St Stephen's Road. This cutting is up to 8 m deep. The reason the sides of this zone of lowered ground are so sheer at the city end (where they are supported by large retaining walls) is that the railway had to be inserted through an already built-up area, and construction in a 'slot' minimised the amount of property that had to be demolished. The line passed through a residential suburb known as Peafield, built during the nineteenth-century expansion that finally saw the city extend beyond the medieval city wall. All three of Norwich's railway stations were located just outside the boundaries of the medieval city. The situation in the Queens Road area was further complicated by the extensive brick workings in that area.

Other examples of local ground level lowering are the cutting of level construction platforms to allow individual buildings to be placed on otherwise sloping ground. This is common where the chalk is present close to the ground surface (in other words, where it 'sub-crops') along valley slopes in the city centre, such as above and below Pottergate and St Benedict's Street. Construction here was relatively easy because the chalk will stand as a near-vertical cut slope (unlike sand), but for long-term stability such cut or 'terraced' sites were usually provided with retaining walls on their upper side.

*Figure 67* Lakenham Way, a former railway cutting, viewed from Southwell Road bridge before the Brazen Gate housing development was built

## Widespread lowering of ground

The most common cause of lowering over a more extensive area than an individual construction platform is for the extraction of raw materials, and we look in more detail at quarrying below. In many areas of the city the legacy of this extraction is not immediately obvious if it has taken place over a wide area, or where locally excavated faces at the quarry edges have been reduced to gentle slopes or masked by later building work.

## The relationship between lowered and raised ground

Because of the effort involved in moving large quantities of soil large distances, there is often something of a balancing effect between lowering and raising of ground in a given vicinity, so areas of filling can be related to nearby sites were the ground has been lowered. Of course, if the ground is being lowered by quarrying for materials to be taken away, there is generally a net loss of material. This is sometimes made up later when the worked area is used for disposal of waste brought in from elsewhere.

In the case of Lakenham Way, much of the contents of the railway cutting may have been used to partly infill a former pit that lay alongside Queens Road adjacent to the line on its way to Victoria Station, so it was a relatively simple thing to move the soil by rail and tip it as the line was constructed. A supermarket has since been built on this partly filled site.

Another neat example of balancing cut and fill is provided by a Victorian drawing showing the proposed construction of a street off Magdalen Road (Figure 68). This was

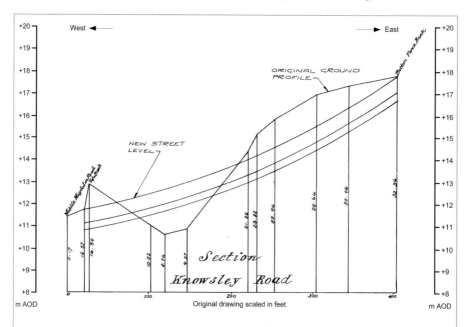

*Figure 68* Cross-section from a plan of 1886 for the development of one of the streets off the east side of Magdalen Road; similar drawings exist for other streets nearby. The original shows relative levels in feet, and the orientation and metric scale have been added.

*Figure 69* The view from Magdalen Road into Knowsley Road, 2012

at a time when the city was expanding over previously quarried areas outside the city wall, and the intended line of the terraced street passed through a chalk pit and up onto the hill behind it. In order to create an acceptable road profile, the solution was to cut the top off the hill, and place the dug material to fill in the hollow. Going up the road today, it may not be obvious that the lowest part of it is constructed over up to about 3 m of filled ground (Figure 69).

## Quarrying

Materials useful for building and other local uses must have been extracted from the ground ever since the first settlers arrived. Even small-scale working is capable of having a profound effect on the landscape if it continues over centuries, but some parts of Norwich were subject to industrial-scale quarrying that changed the landscape in a dramatic fashion over a relatively short period. In some cases this involved moving back complete hillsides. In others, later activities involving filling or other modifications have further resculpted the landscape to leave us a complex legacy.

### Flint and chalk

The cross-section of the city (Figure 14, page 14) shows that the whole of Norwich is underlain at some level by chalk. This is a soft limestone that can be burned to make lime mortar, or turned into other products. The chalk contains many layers of flint (nodules of silica), which in the absence of local building stone is a most useful construction material. The flints can be held together using lime mortar. The very finest flintwork involved trimmed (knapped) flint requiring little or no mortar, such as that visible on the Guildhall and the Bridewell Museum, a wonder of particular interest to the traveller Celia Fiennes when she came to the city in 1698.

The demand for flint and chalk as the medieval city developed should not be under-estimated. The city walls alone extended for more than 3 km. They were 7 m high and over 2 m wide at the base, with most of the dozen gates rising to a height of 10 m and over 6 m wide, and numerous other towers and thickenings. The walls date from the late

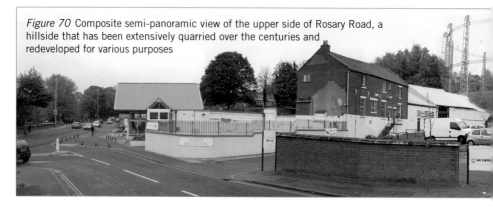

*Figure 70* Composite semi-panoramic view of the upper side of Rosary Road, a hillside that has been extensively quarried over the centuries and redeveloped for various purposes

thirteenth and the fourteenth centuries. A dubious rhyme suggests that stone was hauled up to Norwich from the ruined Roman town at Caistor St Edmund (Venta Icenorum) to build them. Even if we accept that, the masonry represents a very large volume (estimated as 40,000 cubic metres) of locally excavated chalk and flint. The walls also demanded frequent repairs during the following centuries. Many other substantial buildings in Norwich (not least the Castle and Cathedral) are largely composed of the same materials, and the earliest of them were built several centuries before the walls were started. There were also numerous monastic premises and boundary walls built, and a major boom in church reconstruction and extensions during the fifteenth century.

As well as being used for construction purposes, chalk provided quicklime which was used by city industries, and it continued to be excavated into the twentieth century to provide agricultural lime. All this extraction meant that some of Norwich's hills were effectively dug up and taken away out of the city.

We have already seen how chalk is visible as sub-crops along the sides of the river valleys, higher up the slope than river terrace deposits, but at a lower level than the crag or glacial cover forming the higher ground. These outcrops are easy to excavate, so we find most of the major workings on the valley slopes between about +10 and +20 m AOD.

Once they had been started, some quarries were subsequently extended above or below this range of levels. There is usually a limit to how much farther a quarry can be extended into the slope, because of the increasing amount of overburden soil that has to be taken down and the need to support a steeply cut slope. In theory, given the great thickness of chalk available, there is scope for digging downwards tens of metres, but there are clearly disadvantages in having to haul material upwards out of a hole, and also practical difficulties in excavating beneath the water table.

Because chalk was available along several kilometres of valley slope in or within easy reach of the city centre, early quarrying was probably widespread and indiscriminate, with specific deep quarrying locations only developing later as land usage became more intensive. It should be recognised that the working of a hillside is a progressive process, and evidence for earlier quarrying and lime-burning activity may be entirely removed by later working as the hillside moves back.

An example of long-term quarrying is along the **Thorpe hillside** opposite Bishop Bridge. This area must have been particularly attractive for chalk extraction from Norman

times because of its ready access from the Cathedral precinct and city centre via Bishopgate and the Pull's Ferry canal (Figure 70). Looking from the Cathedral, immediately to the right-hand side (south) of what is now Gas Hill was Lollards' Pit. This was a chalk quarry which was used in the sixteenth century for burning at the stake local heretics including Thomas Bilney (in 1531). Reports of the time described the pit as 'being surrounded by rising ground, forming a sort of amphitheatre', but there is no such landform now because of later extensive quarrying through to the nineteenth century. Following this the area was further resculpted to allow it to be used as a gasworks. Ground explo-

Figure 71 Former quarry slope between Horns Lane and Thorn Lane off Ber Street, with industrial units on Garden Street

ration in the vicinity of Lollards' Pit in 1990 and 1998 revealed up to about 7 m of infill extending down to the original bottom of the working at around the level of the water table.

The whole of the Thorpe hillside from Kett's Hill across to St Matthew's Road has been extensively reshaped over the centuries by repeated quarrying, spoil-shifting and redevelopment. It is the hillside visible in the background of Barwell's painting reproduced as Figure 15 on page 15. A remarkable chapter was the creation of The Nest football ground for Norwich City Football Club by infilling a deep chalk quarry in 1908. The pitch was closely bounded by cliff-like retaining walls to create what was again described as an 'amphitheatre' accommodating up to 25,000 spectators in highly

*Figure 72* Southward view across Kett's Cave towards the city centre from Mousehold Avenue

cramped conditions. This must have had the potential for a public disaster, but fortunately that never happened. The club moved to Carrow Road in 1935, and following light industrial and warehouse use, the Nest site is now a residential estate known as the Scholars' Quarter. Meanwhile, the Carrow Road area, on the river flood plain, has itself been much raised over the years by progressive filling.

Early chalk quarrying may also have occurred on the slope **between Ber Street and King Street**. This stretch of hillside, extending for a horizontal distance of some 700

*Figure 74* Development land, 2012, between Drayton Road (right) and Aylsham Road (left) on the site of a former chalk working, annotated to show resculpting of original ground surface

metres, lies entirely within the medieval walled city. There is documentary evidence for lime-burning in places in the thirteenth and sixteenth centuries, but the resulting physical evidence also points to a progression of activity that has left a misshapen slope profile and extensive areas of deeply infilled ground stretching from Carrow Hill right through to Cattle Market Street. Much of this area was covered in terraced housing during the nine-

*Figure 73* Remnant of chalk working on north side of Earlham Road near West Pottergate

teenth century, but structural defects abounded and most of these buildings were cleared in the mid-twentieth century. Bold proposals for high-rise replacement buildings (in addition to Normandie Tower) were abandoned because of difficult ground conditions, and some former quarried sites (such as that lying between Thorn Lane and Horns Lane) have been recolonised by low-quality industrial buildings (Figure 71) or remain as surface car parks.

A further area where chalk and flint quarrying probably went on for centuries was the rising ground on the north side of the Wensum valley above what is now **Barrack Street** (in Pockthorpe). The splendid view of the city from Mousehold Avenue (Figure 72) is over allotments and a playground occupying large former chalk quarries, one of which was known as Kett's Cave on account of a lime kiln and associated tunnel system.

On the opposite (south) side of the river there is also a long history of chalk working along the hillside occupied by **Pottergate** between St Benedict's Street and St Giles

Original ground surface

Street. During what must have been a time of particularly heavy demand for chalk and flint in the fifteenth and sixteenth centuries, and with the city filling up, it is likely that the quarrying activity on this hillside had migrated outside of the city walls. The area outside St Giles Gate was being quarried at this time, with worked faces (and some tunnel accesses) on the lower side of Earlham Road in the area of what is now West Pottergate. This is another highly resculpted part of the city as the result of both the excavation and subsequent infilling, such that much of the physical evidence of deep quarrying is now mostly buried beneath an innocuous-looking slope.

Chalk quarrying and lime burning were also carried on where the raw materials were available along the valley sides **farther out of the city**, probably less intensively in earlier centuries, but becoming more important later on as the city expanded. This included the north and south sides of the Wensum valley upstream of the city (respectively off the Drayton and Dereham roads), within the Dalymond valley to the north (Magdalen Road/Sprowston Road area), and in the Yare valley south of the city (Eaton and Harford).

We therefore have a legacy of quarried faces which are still visible in places to those who look for them (Figures 73 and 74).

### Brickearth

To make bricks, you need soils containing a sufficient content of clay within the mix to hold the bricks together (known as 'cohesive' soils). Most of the soils present in the sequence above the chalk in the central Norwich area consist of sand or gravel, which are non-cohesive soil types, but there is (or was) a most useful layer of sandy clay occurring above the crag. Unsurprisingly, this was in demand for local brickmaking, but this waned from the late nineteenth century when major new brick pits were opened next to the railway line at Peterborough, and it became economic to import mass-produced standardised bricks to the city from elsewhere.

Norwich brickearth occurs as a patchy layer rarely exceeding 5m in thickness at an elevation commonly between about +25 and +30 m AOD over a wide area on higher ground in the northern part of the city, notably in Old Catton, Upper Hellesdon and Mousehold. It was extensively worked in the nineteenth and on into the twentieth centuries to provide bricks to build the expanding suburbs. These brick workings (which also housed the brick kilns) were usually relatively shallow but often extended over wide areas (hence 'brick fields'). Most workings had a near-horizontal base which was often subsequently used to house the brick kilns as the excavated face moved away (Figure 75). In many cases the surviving landform is an excavated slope of a few metres down from the adjacent pre-existing roads. Such slopes can still be seen in residential gardens near the junction of St Clement's Hill and Elm Grove Lane, for example, and near the Sprowston Road roundabout not far from the Brickmakers public house (Figure 76).

Another smaller area of excavatable Norwich brickearth existed on the south side of the city, conveniently just outside the city wall in the Queens Road area. The works in this area were busy at an earlier time than those to the north of the city centre, and must have been responsible for providing a significant proportion of the bricks used to build Georgian Norwich. Much of the evidence is now hidden by filling and subsequent redevelopment, such as the Victorian residential area on the east side of St Stephen's Road opposite the former Norfolk and Norwich Hospital. A large 'brick ground' is shown on Millard and Manning's

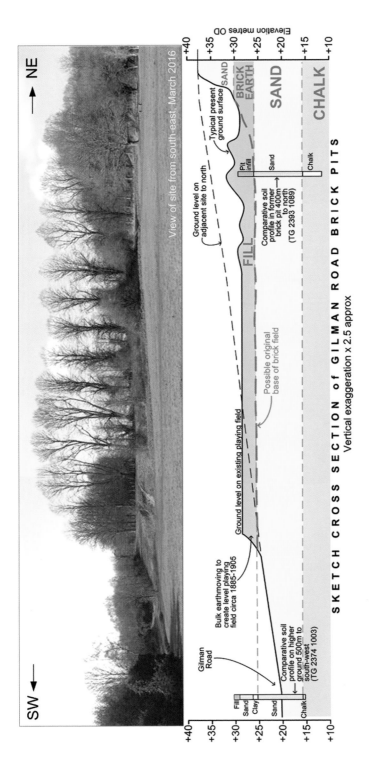

View of site from south-east, March 2016

SW ← → NE

Elevation metres OD

SKETCH CROSS SECTION of GILMAN ROAD BRICK PITS
Vertical exaggeration x 2.5 approx

Figure 75 Speculative cross-section through brick workings off Gilman Road, based on limited ground investigation data

*Figure 76* The Brickmakers public house, Sprowston Road, photographed in 2012

detailed map of 1830 on the site at the junction of Queens Road and Grove Road now occupied by a supermarket and car park (Figure 77). This site remains low in relation to nearby unexcavated ground, but when the present building was constructed on the site of rail sidings and a coal yard in the 1980s, the surface was still found to be

*Figure 77* Comparative views of the former brick field at Queens Road in 1986 and 2010, from Southwell Road bridge (in the opposite direction from Figure 67)

*Figure 78* Postcard
of around 1905
showing the view
from near St James's
Hill, with sand and
gravel workings in the
foreground

*Figure 78* Postcard of around 1905 showing the view from near St James's Hill, with sand and gravel workings in the foreground

underlain by 2–3 m of infill (probably originating from the Lakenham railway cutting). This indicates the original working was dug rather deeper than the present lie of the land would suggest. Probably the same brickearth layer was worked during the nineteenth century in a pit halfway up Long John Hill in Lakenham, where it could be dug from the slope overlooking Yare valley. This former working is now occupied by the Jubilee Community Centre.

## Sand and gravel

Most building operations need a ready supply of gravel and sand for concrete, mortar, drainage and general filling. The natural geology of Norwich means that suitable supplies were unlikely to be far away from any particular construction site. As a consequence there are the remains of many localised workings across the city, especially in the areas of Mousehold and Pockthorpe, where rising ground outside the site made digging and transport of small loads a relatively straightforward matter for builders for many centuries (Figure 78). Sand was also a byproduct of workings intended mainly for chalk or brickearth. As the city developed in the nineteenth and twentieth centuries, there became a need for more controlled supplies on an industrial scale, and large gravel workings were created off Plumstead Road, Heartsease Lane and Harvey Lane. Smaller pits could be found off the main radial roads, such as that off Ipswich Road near Maid Marian Road, now completely infilled.

## Chronology of quarrying

It is worth noting the historical trend in the location of quarries extracting materials to supply the city as it developed. For many years after the Norman conquest, there was sufficient space within the medieval walled city to accommodate quarries and their related industry (such as lime burning), but at some stage these antisocial activities gradually migrated to outside the city. Up until the late eighteenth century when the city gates were removed, most of the building development was within the area enclosed by the medieval city walls, so it was convenient to be quarrying in the areas just outside them. Examples are the chalk pits in the Magdalen Road areas and the brick ground at Queens Road. Once the city had burst out of the walls in the nineteenth century, it was inevitable that many of these worked areas would soon become built over (with some long-term

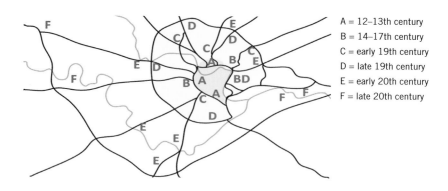

A = 12–13th century
B = 14–17th century
C = early 19th century
D = late 19th century
E = early 20th century
F = late 20th century

*Figure 79* Sketch map of Norwich area showing very generalised time sequence for selected quarrying locations, showing how quarrying tends to move outwards as the city develops

consequences for the stability of foundations), and so the places for quarrying in turn tended to migrate outwards, often to areas just within or outside the present outer ring road. During the mid-twentieth century building boom, the suburbs spread even farther out beyond the outer ring road, again having to deal with former worked areas, and the intensive quarrying activity spreading north-eastward to the far side of Mousehold Heath, and southward into the Yare valley. The process continues to this day, for example with current residential development taking place in the Longwater area (more than 7 km from the city centre) covering an area which was subject to large-scale gravel working up to the late twentieth century (Figure 79).

# 9
# Lost watercourses

## Streams, cockeys and 'underground rivers'

In Chapter 4 we considered how the natural surface drainage operates in Norwich, with most water that has fallen on the ground eventually ending up in either the River Wensum or the River Yare before moving sluggishly off towards Great Yarmouth.

Our topographic map (Figure 26, page 22) indicates how there are several tributary valleys connecting directly to the Wensum, but not one of these contains a visible watercourse today. However, in some cases we do know from historical information that there were once streams (or 'cockeys') running along these routes for at least part of the year, and below we look in more detail at examples of these. They were fed both by surface run-off and by numerous drainage outlets serving earlier development before the implementation of proper underground piped drainage, which only started to become the norm during the late nineteenth and early twentieth centuries.[1] Additionally, we shall cover known examples of other lost watercourses that were little more than river creeks or mooring cuts. Figure 80 shows the watercourses that are described here.

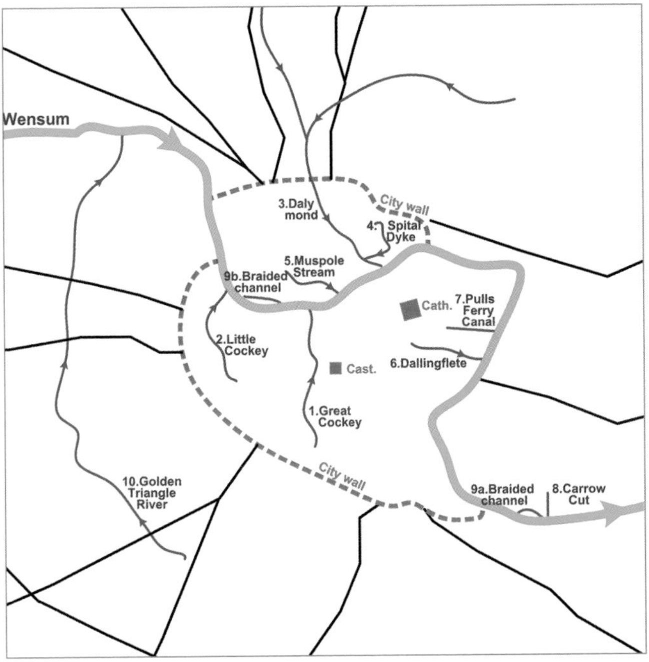

The evidence for some 'lost' watercourses is documentary. That is, they are shown on old maps or referred to in old records or place names (such as Cockey Lane), and their precise alignment may be fossilised in parish or property boundaries, indicating that they must have existed in historic times. In many cases you can still visit the location, 'eye in' where they ran and begin to notice subtle slopes or other remnant features that

*Figure 80* Sketch map (not to scale) showing locations of lost watercourses

---

1  Given the generally sandy soil it is debatable whether many of these streams were actually flowing in postglacial times, before they were 'reactivated' by the process of human development which turned them into drains.

support the documentary evidence. Sometimes there is the opportunity to prove this from the results of intrusive investigation such as boreholes or probe holes.

The evidence for other old watercourses is entirely circumstantial, based on the visible landform, and in these cases it may be that the dry valley is a late glacial feature eroded by temporary meltwater when the otherwise permeable ground was still frozen. In these circumstances it is likely the valley lost its streamflow and became dry thousands of years ago, well before historical time. Examples are the Golden Triangle River and several dry valleys visible on Mousehold Heath (Figure 42, page 34).

Sometimes it is suggested that there are 'underground rivers' beneath the city – a concept some water dowsers like to encourage as they fancy they have indeed 'found' hidden watercourses. That there are discrete flow pathways (or even rivers permanently flowing through natural cave systems) below Norwich is an attractive idea, but unfortunately it is not compatible with our rational understanding of the ground conditions based on geology and hydrology. As we have seen, the ground is entirely saturated from a certain depth beneath our feet in all parts of the city, that particular level being the water table. Its vertical position is relatively easy to predict, and it tends to slope down towards the nearest river at a gradient which is influenced by the permeability of the soil.

There are some 'preferred drainage pathways' in parts of the city where the soil allows more ready lateral passage of groundwater; it's just that these do not really qualify as 'underground rivers'.

## Particular lost watercourses

### The Great Cockey

This is probably the best-known stream that ran through the city centre in historical times, and it had a profound effect on both the local topography and the way the middle part of the city developed. Any Viking settler who sailed up the Wensum into the heart of what is now the city centre would have been impressed by the deep side valley of the Cockey tributary where it ran down the steep chalk slope and joined the main river to the east of what is now Duke Street bridge. The main east–west roadway through the city, probably there in Roman times, had to find its way across this valley, on the line of what is now St Andrew's Street. What is now only a slight dip in the road outside the telephone exchange (Figure 81) was originally a much deeper natural feature, and it is thought there may be the remains of an early bridge or causeway beneath metres of later build-up.

The source of the Great Cockey on the south side of the city centre is thought to have been a hollow in what is now All Saints Green, just inside the line of the city wall. The wet hollow was known as Jack's Pit, and it is possible that it was intermittently fed by spring water or surface run-off shed from the clayey Norwich brickearth which formed the rising ground nearby. The course passed through what became the core of the Norwich Union (Aviva) site north of Surrey Street, across Red Lion Street and down Back of the Inns. This feature was the Cockey or its late-glacial predecessor that eroded out the ground on the western side of Ber Street at its city end (the Wensum valley is on its eastern side), creating a ridge ideal for the construction of the Norman Castle at its northernmost promontory, and physically separating the Castle from the new Norman market place it was deliberately positioned to watch over.

*Figure 81* View across the
Cockey valley along
St Andrew's Street, towards
St Michael at Plea from the
tower of St Lawrence, 2009

By the time the Cockey
had crossed the present
Davey Place, it was flowing
across the chalk subcrop in
what was probably a mini
ravine, as referred to on
page 54. It must have been
a significant physical barrier
for occupiers, and became
a site for the accumulation
of soil and refuse in late
medieval times.

The stream course
continued to fall steeply
across the chalk outcrop as
it crossed London Street
(formerly Cockey Lane)
and Bedford Street, and ran
down what is now a small
thoroughfare called School
Lane (previously Little
Cockey Lane) to the rear of
the telephone exchange. Intrusive investigation here showed the stream bed falling close
to +1 m AOD in this area, which is similar to the water level in the River Wensum, and
would put the level of the stream bed some
5 m below the present level of St Andrew's
Street where it crosses (Figure 81).

It is likely that the Great Cockey
originally dissipated into the marshland
previously existing below St Andrew's
multi-storey car park (see Figure 58 on
page 50). This low-lying site was reclaimed
to construct the Duke of Norfolk's palace
around 1540; probably the stream was
directed along the east side of the site, and
it might have provided handy moorings.
The position of the Great Cockey is still

*Figure 82* Storm sewer outfall on the north
bank of the River Wensum, on the line of the
former Great Cockey

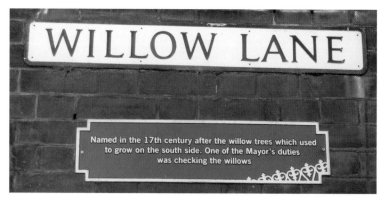

visible, represented by a culvert outfall in the modern river wall to the rear of Duke's Palace Wharf, facing the Playhouse garden (Figure 82).

## The Little Cockey

This stream provided drainage to the west part of the city centre, and connected to a pit in the middle of Bethel Street close to its junction with St Giles Street, explaining the intriguing curvature in the present road alignment that remains to this day. The source might have been at the corner of Theatre Street and Chapelfield East, where anomalous peaty deposits were found in the early 1980s during the construction of Dencora House. The stream ran steeply down (again across the chalk outcrop) alongside Willow Lane on its south side, providing suitable conditions for that water-loving tree type (Figure 83), then across Potter-gate and St Benedict's Street, where a subtle dip in the road can still be detected aligned

to the curving lane on the west side of St Swithin's Church (Figure 84). It then crossed Westwick Street, arriving into the river about 100 m downstream from New Mills.

## The Dalymond

Our topographic map of Norwich shows a sizeable tributary valley running from the north to join the River Wensum at a point about 700 m upstream of its big bend. The scale of this valley probably reflects its importance for drainage in the late Ice Age rather than a major watercourse in historic times. Its course through the northern suburbs is quite easy to follow to this day, down Catton Grove Road and Angel Road, joined on

*Figure 84* Westward view along St Benedict's Street near to where the Little Cockey crossed from left to right

*Figure 85* Deep foundation excavations for new houses fronting Magpie Road, where the former Dalymond valley has been partly infilled

the line of Denmark Road and Waterloo Road by a sub-tributary draining Mousehold Heath (now the dry valley of Valley Drive). However, its route across Magpie Road is masked by high-density Victorian residential development in the Heath Road area that may have involved raising ground levels to partially infill the valley (Figures 85 and 86). As it crosses the line of the inner ring road the course of the Dalymond is even more obscured by centuries of occupation and development, not least the Anglia Square complex and flyover which sadly obliterated Stump Cross, the branching junction of Magdalen Street and the original Botolph Street. The watercourse ran on the north side of that street, in a south-easterly direction across what is now a public car park close to St Saviour's Church. It then turned slightly eastward to cut Fishergate halfway along, outfalling into the river at the position of Hansard Lane next to St Edmund's Church.

## Spital Dyke

This was a small but archaeologically significant watercourse that joined the Dalymond from the north just before it crossed Fishergate. Judging from the line of old property

*Figure 86* Northward view in 2010 from the now-closed Anglia Square multistorey car park, showing the approximate line of the Dalymond stream entering the medieval city near the junction of Heath Road and Magpie Road

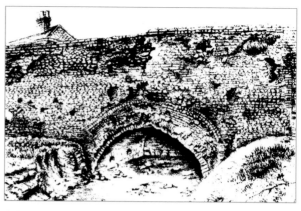

*Figure 87* The stone bridge at Horsefair pictured in 1888, prior to development of the terraced houses on St Faith's Lane when the ditch was infilled. The house roof visible above the parapet still stands.

boundaries, it seems to have run between St James's Church (the Puppet Theatre) and the former St Paul's church (this occupied the site diagonally across the present roundabout from St James, until destroyed in World War Two).

The line of this stream and the parallel former Cowgate Street (Whitefriars) probably mark the position of the eastern side of the horseshoe-shaped Anglo-Scandinavian fortifications (page 47).

## Muspole Stream

The curious bend to Muspole Street at its Colegate end, instead of running straight across to Water Lane, is thought to be the result of its being diverted to the west side of a pre-existing pond (the Mus Pool), possibly during the fifteenth century, when the adjacent St George's Church was extended with a tower. A ground-probing exercise confirmed that a pond lay beneath what is now the west lawn of the churchyard (since raised by burials), and it was probably a general sump for drainage from a nearby area of marginal ground that has been gradually reclaimed from marshland (Figure 88). Its outflow was a small watercourse that ran down Colegate in the direction of Fye Bridge, before turning to cross beneath what is now Friars Quay, on a diagonal line only preserved now by the parish boundary, to reach the river at a point somewhere near the slipway.

## Dallingflete

Unsurprisingly, the Tombland area, one of the earliest occupied parts of the city, was drained by a watercourse passing down onto the nearby flood plain, and this is still visible at the point where it reaches the Wensum as a ditch crossed by a small bridge carrying the riverside walk, approximately 80 m south of Pull's Ferry.

The start of the Dallingflete can be traced roughly where the Norwich School sports hall is on St Faith's Lane, and it ran down the river terrace across the line of the later Cathedral Street to pass below St Faith's Lane near its junction with Recorder Road. An ancient bridge survived here right up to Victorian times (Figure 87), before nineteenth-century housing development in this area led to the filling-in of the watercourse. The bridge is mentioned in publicity leaflets for the nearby Hills & Underwood vinegar factory (Figure 89), and its remains may still exist beneath the roadway.

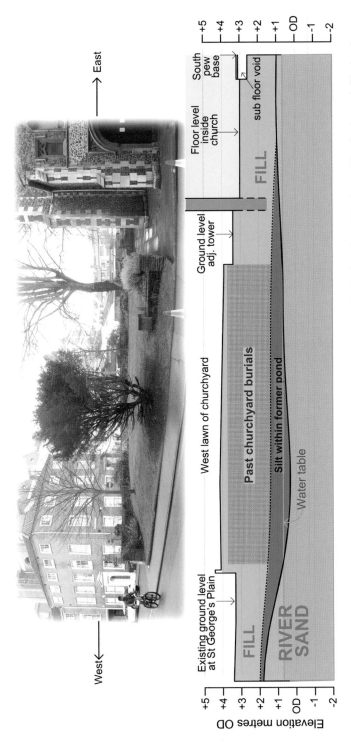

*Figure 88* Schematic cross-section through the lawn west of St George Colegate, which may be the location of the former Mus Pool, now infilled and raised. The conjectural soil boundaries are based on limited information and contextual information.

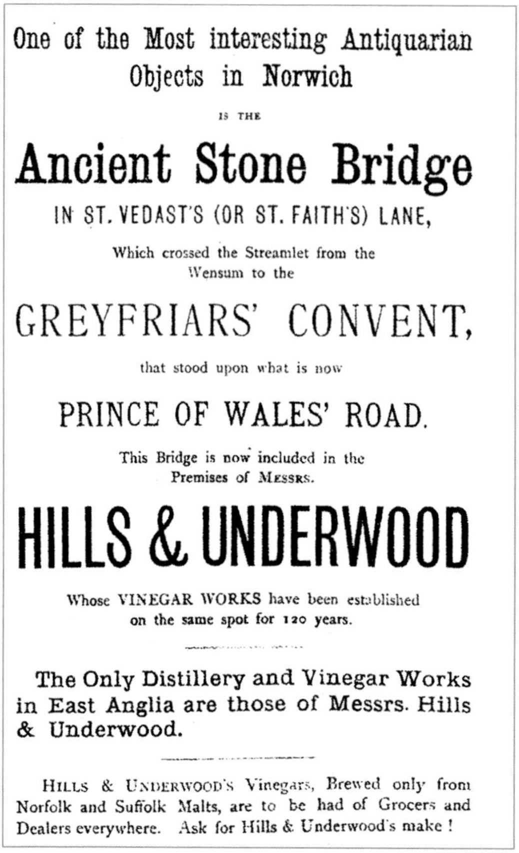

One of the Most interesting Antiquarian
Objects in Norwich

IS THE

# Ancient Stone Bridge

IN ST. VEDAST'S (OR ST. FAITH'S) LANE,

Which crossed the Streamlet from the
Wensum to the

# GREYFRIARS' CONVENT,

that stood upon what is now

## PRINCE OF WALES' ROAD.

This Bridge is now included in the
Premises of Messrs.

# HILLS & UNDERWOOD

Whose VINEGAR WORKS have been established
on the same spot for 120 years.

**The Only Distillery and Vinegar Works
in East Anglia are those of Messrs. Hills
& Underwood.**

HILLS & UNDERWOOD'S Vinegars, Brewed only from
Norfolk and Suffolk Malts, are to be had of Grocers and
Dealers everywhere. Ask for Hills & Underwood's make!

*Figure 89* Nineteenth-century handbill for the Hills & Underwood vinegar factory, mentioning the ancient bridge

## Pull's Ferry Canal

Another nearby watercourse across the flood plain was the 250 m long navigable channel cut by the Normans to provide waterborne access to the Cathedral precinct in the area of the Lower Close. The water gate at the river end now appears wider than it is high because the water channel it straddles has been filled in, but views dating from the mid-eighteenth century when the watercourse was still in place (Figure 90) show the free-standing arch of the watergate as a relatively tall structure. We know from contemporary maps that the line of the channel lies slightly to the north of that of Ferry Road, as evidenced by the signs of historic subsidence movement affecting various buildings built across the weak infilled ground.

## Carrow Cut

For much of the history of Norwich, the low-lying ground on the east side of the Wensum downstream from what is now Foundry Bridge was simply grazing meadows, owned by the Dean and Chapter. This is a far cry from today's busy football stadium and Riverside complex which followed on from twentieth-century industrial development. This marshy land lay outside the medieval city, and with the river was effectively part of its defences, overlooked by the rising ground west of King Street. At the time of Joseph Manning's map of the city in 1834, the only building on that side of the river was a large red brick maltings (Figure 91) that had been built ten years earlier on the north-west side of the then Carrow Road, which linked the original Carrow Bridge in Colman's Works across to Thorpe. In the mid-nineteenth century a wide navigable cut was made to link the maltings directly to the river, and this watercourse survived the arrival of the football stadium in 1935, remaining until the 1970s when it was infilled to make more car parking space in the area directly behind Norwich City's South Stand. Sadly the fine maltings themselves became a victim of the success of the football team, being sacrificed in 2003 to allow replacement of the original south stand by the larger Jarrold Stand (since renamed several times).

*Figure 90* Extract from *South-east Prospect of Norwich*, engaving by Samuel and Nathaniel Buck, 1741

## Braided river channels

We have already seen (page 3) that there used to be a side-branch of the River Wensum affecting land off Coslany Street, crossed by a little bridge painted by John Crome. This was not the only side channel in the immediate vicinity, as shown by seventeenth and eighteenth-century maps: for example, Thomas Cleer's map of around 1696 shows another branch on the opposite side of the river, slightly downstream. It is thought there were originally two bridges carrying Coslany Street across the braided river channel (Figure 92). Indeed, the early English name 'Coslany' is thought to mean 'an island among river marshes'. It is clear that the combined effects of filling and canalisation (see page 52) have greatly changed the original natural landform in this part of the city.

There is evidence for a similar braiding of the river channel immediately downstream of the city at Carrow. Excavations beneath the Norwich City Jarrold Stand revealed a sandy island beneath the more recent peat deposits, the archaeological interest being in the finding of flint chippings dating from Upper Palaeolithic times (10,000–50,000 years ago), the earliest evidence of occupation in the Norwich area.

### The Golden Triangle River

Residents of the streets off Unthank Road will probably be familiar with some remarkable steep slopes on the sides of a

*Figure 91* Carrow Maltings under demolition in 2003

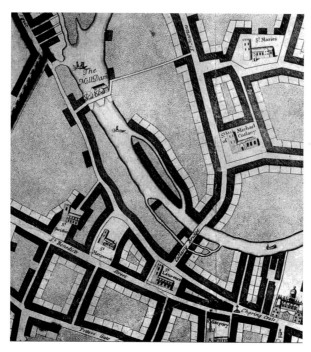

Figure 92 Extract from Thomas Cleer's map of 1696, showing the braided river channel at Coslany

valley-like feature passing obliquely through the Golden Triangle area. This valley is clearly visible on our topographic map (page 22), and like the course of the Dalymond, is almost certainly the remnant of a drainage course at the end of the Ice Age. No watercourse as such seems to be shown on any historic maps. It begins as a slight dip affecting Ipswich Road outside City College and crossing Newmarket Road near Albert Terrace. It then becomes a more obvious feature at Newmarket Street (Figure 93), crossing Unthank Road diagonally from Gloucester Street through to Portersfield Road, Park Lane and West Parade. Earlham Road, a former turnpike, was raised on a causeway as it crossed the valley, but the valley continues as the lowest point of Stafford Street, and then runs off in the direction of Old Palace Road towards a probable connection to the Wensum in the Heigham Street area.

Figure 93 South-westward view along Newmarket Street, which crosses the valley of the 'Golden Triangle River'

# 10
# Flooding in Norwich

Norwich has been affected by flooding from time to time, notably in 1912, which to judge by the flood plates was the worst recorded event affecting the city as a whole (Figure 94). While flooding by definition refers to water rising temporarily above ground level, this account is included in my study of the city from ground level downwards because subterranean factors were involved.

A distinction needs to be made here between different types of flooding. While the river downstream of New Mills is close to sea level and subject to some tidal fluctuation, Norwich is sufficiently far from the sea not to have been badly affected by tidal surges – such as that of January 1953, which affected coastal Norfolk with tragic consequences. Norwich is however subject to fluvial flooding, caused by water coming down the river from the large Wensum catchment, and that is what happened in August 1912 as well as on a number of previous occasions. To 'natural' fluvial flooding we must also add the more modern human-caused factor of flash flooding created by the instant run-off from hard-paved urban surfacing, which can quickly lead to the overloading of underground piped drainage systems.

Nowadays you can normally expect to walk across the city centre from south to north (say from St Stephen's Street to Anglia Square) without getting your feet wet or even muddy, but of course this has been possible only since the construction of river crossings, street paving and some major filling of previously low-lying areas. During the early stages of historical development (from Anglo-Scandinavian times), large areas of the city were still low-lying marshland. They were on a river flood plain which was subject to intermittent inundation as a

*Figure 94* Flood level plate at New Mills Yard, pictured in 1961, showing the 1912 flood as the highest

*Figure 95* The view upstream from St Miles' Bridge, Coslany Street, still showing a degree of canalisation that was typical of much of the city before stretches were widened in the 1920s and 1930s

temporary 'sponge' to store excess river water until it could drain away again (Figure 56 on page 50). The organic nature of the soil (peat and silt) and proximity of the water table in the ground at around river level meant that people could not rely on being able to cross this area easily on foot, except perhaps during high summer. It is no surprise that the important routes, such as that leading to the river crossing near Bishop Bridge, were soon provided with an approach on a raised embankment above the adjacent marsh level, and early bridge crossings may well have been connected by raised timber causeways, such as the one found at Fye Bridge Street probably dating from the tenth century.

Elsewhere, because of the importance of direct access to the river it was necessary to stabilise the muddy surface to avoid getting bogged down underfoot, as we have seen (pages 50–1). Over time, vertical river frontages were constructed and there was widespread, progressive raising of the riverside areas and consequent loss of the natural flood plains, coupled with narrowing of the river (Figure 95).

It was inevitable that this gradual canalisation of the river would eventually have consequences, in that in the built-up parts of the city there was no longer the possibility of a full river occasionally spreading onto its flood plain. Instead the confined water can only rise up the river walls and overspill onto streets and into adjacent buildings. It may not be coincidence that although serious floods were recorded in 1570, 1614, 1646, 1734, 1762, 1770 and 1878, the highest flood took place in 1912, by which time it could be argued the human-made causal factors had reached their greatest extent. This particular flood episode, in late August, followed a truly exceptional 190 mm of summer rainfall in 48 hours. This by chance centred on the Wensum catchment in central Norfolk.

Comparison of the 1912 flood levels recorded on flood plates in different parts of the city shows that the absolute height of the flood level (in m AOD) decreased as we move downstream through the city, from over +4.5 m AOD upstream of New Mills to below +2.5 m

*Figure 96* Southward view towards the rear of houses fronting Heigham Street, from the flooded sidings at City Station, in late August 1912. The floodwater is standing at about +4.3 m AOD.

AOD downstream of Carrow. The greatest overspilling from the rising river level occurred where there was the least difference between normal river level and the top of the river wall. That is the situation just upstream of New Mills, which explains why the area around Heigham Street, Lothian Street, Barn Road and the City Station was hit hardest by flooding. These are the only areas where contemporary photographs show water more than knee deep

*Figure 97* The flood-damaged Norwich Mercury Works viewed from St George's Bridge in 1912, accurately superimposed on the modern view towards the river bank to the rear of the Playhouse garden

(Figure 96). This floodwater subsequently flowed over the surface into the lower parts of the city centre to add to that overtopping the river walls elsewhere.

The city authorities recognised the problem of river canalisation, and over the following two decades deliberate measures were taken to widen the river in places to increase the water capacity and hence reduce the flood risk. The river edge was moved back by up to 12 m in stretches upstream and downstream from Fye Bridge (to the rear of Colegate and Fishergate), and new concrete river walls were built which can be seen to this day. Fye Bridge was lengthened accordingly (and the road was simultaneously widened) in 1932, while the preserved St George's Bridge necessarily remained as a pinch point. River widening was readily made immediately upstream thanks to the washing away in 1912 of the Norwich Mercury building, which originally stood well out into the river from the present Norwich Playhouse garden (Figure 97). Ironically, the river has recently been narrowed again at this same point following the construction in 2002 of a new river wall on the opposite bank, to the rear of Duke's Palace Wharf. Do we ever learn?

# Part III

# Riddled with tunnels?

*Figure 98* Bus-in-hole carving in The Dell park, Earlham Road

*Figure 99* A visual representation of the physical Norwich often portrayed by local and national media

# 11
## Myths and their plausibility

### Unexpected events

In Earlham Road in March 1988 a red bus sank into a hole that had opened up suddenly in the road surface. Photos of the rear-engined vehicle with its front wheels in the air (Figure 100) acquired iconic status. Among other things, this image sent a young advertising executive's career into orbit when he came up with the line 'Nothing fills a hole like a double-decker' to promote a Cadbury's chocolate bar.[1] It goes without saying there was both disruption and concern (Figure 101).

Barely a month earlier the rear part of a terrace house in Kett's Hill had fallen into a very deep hole in the ground, making another dramatic picture. Local journalists gleefully reported the rumour that the woman who lived there had been in the bath at the time. Needless to say this was a tale without foundation (so to speak), although the owner was evidently at home when the collapse occurred (Figure 102).

So 1988 was memorable for subsidence in Norwich, and not least for me, because I helped start up a site investigation firm that year. The 'bus in the hole' incident actually happened when I was midway through a month's break between leaving a local construction

*Figure 100* One of several widely circulated images of the bus-in-hole incident of 3 March 1988, as quickly commandeered for the Cadbury's advertising campaign

---

1   Sadly, of course, this was not one of the products from Norwich's Rowntree Mackintosh factory at Chapelfield, just along the road.

Figure 101 The bus incident as it looked to a passer-by on Earlham Road, with British Gas in attendance

firm and our newly formed company starting to trade. We could not have asked for more timely public focus on matters subterranean and the desirability of investigating ground conditions.

Although the bus incident has over-shadowed the topic in recent times, many other subsid-ence events, generally less dramatic, have fuelled Norwich's reputation for being, in the journalists' cliché, 'riddled with tunnels' or similar. It is a stock description often inserted to pad out any report of a hole opening up. Such incidents are often linked to the collapse of underground chalk workings, but this is not always the case.

If it were easier to distinguish tunnel-related incidents from other types of hole in the ground, it would be apparent that those areas of the city directly affected by chalk mines are geographically rather limited. Some small localities perhaps come close to qualifying as 'riddled', but it is not at all accurate to pin this description on the city as a whole.

Perhaps the most traumatic of all subsidence events in the city to date was the sudden overnight collapse of the internal walls of a terrace house in Merton Road in May 1936, killing two elderly occupants (Figure 103), Mr and Mrs Hall. Their bodies were recovered five days later from a depth of 12 m below ground level. This was indisputably tragic, but in geographical terms it was not an isolated event. A major collapse had affected the same street in November 1927 (Figure 104). Much investigation and stabilisation work was carried out then and has been since.

A serious attempt was made in the 1980s to compile a systematic historic record of the city's tunnels and the incidents related to them. (This information is held by Norwich City Council.) And consulting engineers Howard Humphreys & Partners provided an account of the history of subsidence in a report for central government in 1993.[2]

The risks and causes of this kind of collapse are now well understood. Although rather less was known in the 1930s, in hindsight that subsidence with terrible consequences in Merton Road could have been predicted. However, people were of course shocked and worried at the time. The effect on public perception was only overtaken by the impact of the Blitz six years later.

The concept of 'Subterranean Norwich' has been around quite a long time. A newspaper

2    See the Further Reading on page 151.

The rear of the house in Kett's Hill

Figure 102 Not always accurate local press coverage of the subsidence incident affecting the rear of number 69a Kett's Hill on 30 January 1988

Figure 103 Aftermath of the collapse of the rear of a terraced house at 50 Merton Road on 11 May 1936

*Figure 104* A major collapse in Merton Road on 11 November 1927, eight years before the fatal incident nearby

article of 1930 (Figure 105) reported it as the name given to a public attraction more than a hundred years earlier: 'In 1824 the show was boosted by local advertisements announcing "the beautiful and extensive vaults lately discovered under the hill by St Giles' Gates will be open during the Assize and following week. Admission 1s. Experienced guides will conduct the company round."' So 'Subterranean Norwich' originally referred to a set of tunnels related to chalk mining just outside the city walls at Earlham Road, very close to where the bus sank 164 years later.

It is thought these particular workings dated from the sixteenth century. A name, 'John Bond', and date, '1571', were found inscribed on a tunnel wall, and that date fits other evidence. The same newspaper went on in 1939 to publish a copy of a detailed plan of the mine system (originally drawn in 1823 after the tunnels had

> LOCAL CHALK CAVES."
> "Subterranean Norwich" was a popular attraction a hundred years ago; and during the Assize week the St. Giles' "caves" were on exhibition. In 1824 the show was boomed by local advertisements announcing "The beautiful and extensive vaults lately discovered under the hill by St. Giles' Gates will be open during the Assize and following week. Admission, 1s. Experienced guides will conduct the company round." Chalk-pits abounded in this district, and many years ago caves were cut through the mill in various directions and of considerable length. These workings for chalk had been carried out at various periods; and the tunnellings were pushed far into the hill. Some of the old caves thus created were used in later

*Figure 105* Extract from an article in the *Eastern Daily Press* on 22 March 1930 describing the original 'Subterranean Norwich' attraction

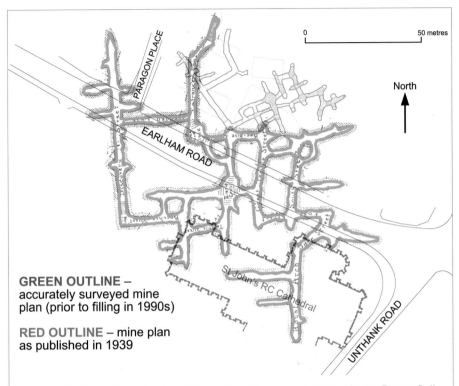

0          50 metres

North

PARAGON PLACE

EARLHAM ROAD

St John's RC Cathedral

UNTHANK ROAD

**GREEN OUTLINE –**
accurately surveyed mine
plan (prior to filling in 1990s)

**RED OUTLINE** – mine plan
as published in 1939

*Figure 106* Comparison of a plan of the Earlham Road mine published in the *Eastern Daily Press* in December 1939 (in red) with the more recently verified position of the same tunnel system (in green). The original was based on an 1823 plan which was fairly accurate but reproduced in the newspaper at the wrong scale and orientation in relation to the modern street layout. These tunnels are at around +12 to +14 m AOD.

been rediscovered) superimposed on the present road layout (Figure 106). The tunnels had been given their names by the nineteenth-century tourist guides. This plan caused a stir at the time of publication because it seemed to show that the workings extended beneath Earlham Road and also beneath the relatively newly built St John's Roman Catholic Church (now Cathedral). After some correspondence it was determined that the drawing had mistakenly been reproduced at the wrong scale and also at a slightly incorrect orientation. This error was further compounded by another plan, rescaled but still wrong, published in the newspaper in 1984. Thankfully the tunnel system in question did not affect the Cathedral site, although it did extend below existing buildings on the opposite side of the road. It has since been backfilled. This was not unique as an example of the increased alarm that can be caused by misinformation.

To see how common it is to think of Norwich as being 'riddled with tunnels', you only have to Google a couple of relevant terms to find numerous accounts of ancient secret thoroughfares criss-crossing beneath the city and linking various landmarks. Just a small selection of the linkages claimed to exist is given in Figure 107. While far from comprehensive, it reflects the variety of locations that feature. The detailed geology at these sites is equally varied. The sheer number of tunnel myths in Norwich may have accumulated because of the nature of the ground, but it is also a reflection of the intensity of human activity over the centuries in a busy and successful city. It is often claimed that these underground links were used by people involved in illicit activities, adventures or heroic escapes, and these rumours help such stories to persist.

While tunnels undoubtedly do exist in places, these tales have proliferated as a result of some combination of vivid imaginations, wishful thinking, journalistic licence, a natural reluctance on the part of the City Council to release information, the presence of a major insurance company in the city, and a tendency for those who have actually visited tunnel systems to consistently exaggerate their size (typically by a factor of three) when they emerge. Professionals bear some of the blame too. When surveyors and structural engineers cannot see beneath the surface, it is always safer for them to suggest that tunnels *could* be there than to guarantee they are not. It might not reassure their clients, but it protects them from future claims for damages.

Often holes that open up in roads turn out to be caused by collapsed sewers (Figure 108). In some cases, they are caused by the slumping of soil into natural 'solution features' which can extend to a very great depth, although even these are often activated or intercepted by human-made activities at a higher level.

Although the tunnel stories range from the ridiculous right through to the proven, in practice most lie somewhere in between these extremes. To help separate tunnel fact from tunnel fiction, it is useful to consider the natural geology, the scale of underground passageways we do know about, and why they are there.

## Geological factors

Our rational model for the geology and hydrogeology of the city (outlined in Part I) gives us the means to assess the likelihood of particular alleged tunnel routes.

◆   Castle to the Guildhall, to Carrow Priory (in the grounds of the old Colman's Works in Bracondale) and to the Cathedral
◆   Cathedral to the Samson & Hercules, Tombland, to Princes Street, and to St Benet's Abbey at Ludham
◆   Guildhall to the former City Gaol at St Giles Gate (now site of St John's RC Cathedral)
◆   Upper King Street (the Compasses pub) to Pull's Ferry
◆   Princes Street (Princes Inn) to St Andrew's Hall
◆   St Andrew's Hall to St George's Street (Red Lion)
◆   Lower Goat Lane (the Raven) to St Giles Gate
◆   Charing Cross (Shrub House) to St Benedict's Gate
◆   Fye Bridge Street (Mischief Tavern) to St Clement's Church
◆   Maid's Head Hotel to Cathedral Close
◆   Barrack Street (Pockthorpe Brewery) to Kett's Cave, Anchor Street

*Figure 107* A selection of tunnel myths, quickly compiled from an internet search

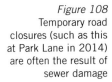

*Figure 108*
Temporary road
closures (such as this
at Park Lane in 2014)
are often the result of
sewer damage

Where the ground in question is composed of chalk and lies above the water table, this is in theory an ideal situation for mining, as the roof is likely to be able to stand unsupported. Nevertheless digging tunnels for any distance remains hard work. A more problematic geological situation is, for example, an attempt to dig a tunnel through sand and gravel, which would have to be lined all the way (probably in brickwork) to avoid immediate collapse. Similarly, a tunnel passing beneath the water table would present even more difficult practical engineering challenges.

In no way can we discount the possibility of there being tunnels linking adjacent cellars of buildings lying on a similar contour on the dry chalk in (say) the Pottergate/ Bedford Street area. On the other hand, tales of a 15 km long tunnel leading all the way to Ludham from Norwich (Figure 107) are extremely far-fetched. As with any tunnel which would involve crossing beneath a river where the ground is saturated, users would have needed an aqualung! The same is probably true for any tunnels said to pass beneath the line of the Great Cockey in the city centre, which makes it doubtful that the commonly quoted link between the Castle and the Guildhall actually existed. This myth may have derived from a mistaken reference to the prisoners' tunnel which certainly exists, linking the Castle Gaol to the nearby Shirehall courts (Figure 109).

## Matters of scale

People living elsewhere in the country, when reading about the bus in the hole and similar happenings, could be forgiven for concluding that

*Figure 109* A brick-lined tunnel leads from the former cells beneath the castle keep to the rear of the Shirehall on Market Avenue, and is occasionally open to tourist visitors

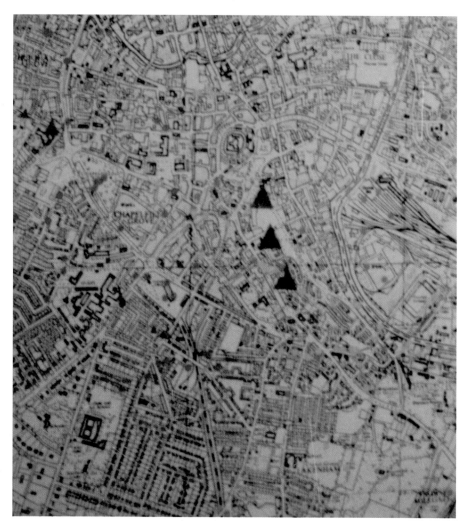

*Figure 110* Extract from a board-mounted plan previously displayed in the City Engineer's Department. The dark green triangles indicated known subsidences, and are scaled at some 60 m across. The coloured dots recorded Second World War bomb drops.

Norwich is in its entirety a problem location for underground workings. I was once shown a regional map (in the office of a national organisation) of geological problems of East Anglia, which had a large orange blob covering the whole of the city (and smaller blobs on Thetford and Bury St Edmunds). Even the City Council used to have a map of Norwich on display at a reception desk with particular streets (such as Thorn Lane or Kett's Hill) awarded a dark green triangle to show that a subsidence event had been recorded there (Figure 110). You can imagine this caused real problems for people wanting to sell houses in these locations that they had believed were built on solid ground.

Geological factors are not normally aligned with particular streets or postcodes. In practice, holes that open up related to underground workings, while usually deep, are

# Fresh menace of crumbling tunnels

By Mark Leslie

CRUMBLING chalk workings menacing city homes could be more widespread than first feared, according to a new report.

The survey into subsidence in Dell Crescent found that huge 12ft high underground tunnels stretched too far to be safely charted.

"Without doubt it is certain the chalk workings are more extensive than those revealed by the present subsidence," the report to tomorrow's environmental health committee says.

**PRIVATE LAND**

Surveyors said it was unsafe to tunnel through collapses blocking the tunnels to see how far the mine workings extend, but most must be under private land and therefore not the responsibility of the council.

The area under Dell Crescent which collapsed on January 7 has been filled with concrete. But no action is proposed for the tunnels spreading under private houses and also threatening a Scout hut off the Dereham Road.

"It is absolutely heartbreaking," said Mrs Valerie Rudd, a nurse who faces a year out of her home due to subsidence.

"It is disgusting," said neighbour Mr Eddie Jenkins. "This past month has been one of

*Figure 111* Cutting from the *Evening News*, 12 February 1990, speculating on the extent of tunnels discovered following a collapse at Dell Crescent, off Dereham Road. This tunnel is at +12 to +15 m AOD.

often only a few metres across. So they are very localised, and usually affect only one part of a plot, and certainly not the whole of a road, most of which may be perfectly sound. However it is difficult (and very expensive) to carry out a high enough intensity of ground investigation to be absolutely sure that there is no subsidence risk to a particular site, and neither is it easy to acquire enough detail to produce meaningful maps highlighting 'risk areas', so often some doubt does remain.

The potential horizontal length of workings is often overestimated by those who have never tried digging one. People often unjustifiably extrapolate where tunnels might lead from inadequate evidence, and they are not always as straight as they anticipate (Figure 111). High-tech geophysical methods of investigating the ground from the surface using radar or resistivity have been tried for detecting voids at depth, but even on flat and open ground (a luxury in the built-up area) these are rarely as successful as they are for shallow archaeological work. No amount of expert 'interpretation' can overcome the inherent problem that the 'noise' from relatively small variations in the ground at shallow depths masks the signal from large variations at greater depths, so deep tunnels can easily be missed. At best, such methods tend to generate the need for further investigation of anomalies using direct methods such as probing, boring or direct excavation.

## Why go underground anyway?

Chalk has been extracted for many centuries in Norwich to provide lime and flints which are used for construction and other purposes, as described on pages 61–6. The buildings and city walls contain a huge volume of this material. While all of Norwich is underlain by chalk, only in certain parts of the city is it close enough to the surface to be easily accessible by digging. The easiest way to obtain it is to dig from an open pit in a valley side, and there are many places along the city's valleys where this has been done, from medieval right through to Victorian times, with some pits still working into the twentieth century. As we have already seen, the exposure of the chalk lies between the river sediments on the valley bottom and the covering crag and glacial strata at a higher level. This approximates to an elevation above sea level of between about 5 and 20 m (+5 to +20 m AOD). This conveniently confines the area of significant tunnel risk to the valley-side parts of the city rising from that sort of elevation.

There is however a constraint on how deep chalk quarries can be excavated, because they will eventually encounter groundwater and also because of the effort needed to haul the chalk out. There is also a limit in how far back into the hillside they can be dug, because of the amount of overburden to remove and the limits to land ownership.

One of the characteristics of chalk in Norwich (in contrast to other UK localities) is that it is relatively soft and easily dug, but at the same time it is strong enough for tunnels through it to be able to stand unsupported. So you can see how mines started to be dug as tunnels back into the hillsides, and these could readily be extended over time.

The earlier hand-dug tunnels tended to be more haphazard in plan than the later

ones, which might be of sufficient size to allow a horse-drawn cart to remove the chalk. Some grid-like Victorian and later tunnel systems evidently used a system of trucks on rails hauled by rope.

Typical tunnel lengths range in Norwich from a few metres to tens of metres, but never up into the kilometres scale. The greatest straight-line distance between the quarry face and the farthest mined tunnel recorded in the city is some 85 m, at Harford Hills. Even if we were to assume that mines could affect say 100 metres of ground back from all chalk quarries, only a tiny

*Figure 112* Deep cellar below the Birdcage public house, Pottergate. The cellar floor is at around +14 m AOD.

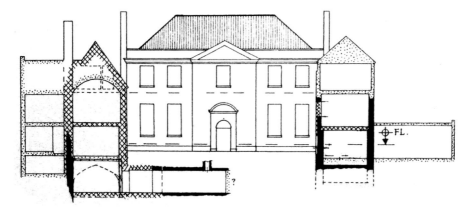

*Figure 113* Cross-section of the Assembly House (viewed from Theatre Street) showing the position of the medieval undercroft extending beneath the front courtyard. This is a remnant from the former College of St Mary in the Fields, and exists at a level of around +24 m AOD.

percentage of occupied Norwich would be affected. The tragic Merton Road collapse of 1936 took place within just 25 m of a worked chalk face, abutting the deep pit that previously existed beneath what is now the car park of Norwich Community Hospital.

## Building downwards

It should not be forgotten that besides tunnels for chalk mining, there are many other types of man-made underground opening, including wells, also numerous cellars, crypts and undercrofts originally used for storage, and often with brick-lined arches looking as if they should lead somewhere.

It is noticeable how both cellars and the more ancient undercrofts are concentrated in those areas of the city centre where the buildings are founded directly on chalk. An example is the area between Pottergate and Bank Plain (Figure 112). There are also examples of brick-arched and barrel-vaulted undercrofts constructed in the sand at a higher level than the chalk, such as that beneath the Assembly House forecourt (Figures 113 and 114). Norwich has over 50 undercrofts surviving largely intact, more than any other town or city in the United Kingdom.

When it comes to counting the city's air-raid shelters, only one pre-existing quarry tunnel system was significantly adapted for public use in the run-up to World War Two (at Rosary Road: see pages 100–1). In the event most underground public shelters were specially constructed from the ground surface by digging linear trenches in school play-grounds and parks, lining them in concrete panels and covering them over. Many of these have now been stabilised by grubbing out the linings and/or filling the trench with compacted soil, but some survive intact, such as one forgotten then recently rediscovered beneath the playground of Bignold School.

From the late nineteenth century, some much deeper and longer tunnels were dug by hand or machine though the chalk and lined with brickwork or concrete segments for the purpose of foul sewers, storm water drainage and service ducts (see pages 104–6).

*Figure 114  (above and below)* Two views of the large undercroft at the Assembly House, with both brick-vaulted and barrel-vaulted sections

# 12
# Known tunnel systems

## Where are the historic chalk workings?

In several areas of the city where the chalk is accessible on the valley sides, limited tunnel systems have been found, usually directly associated with chalk pits and lime kilns. Occasionally there are also vertical shafts, such as that implicated in the collapse at Kett's Hill in 1988 (page 89).

Such areas include the slopes above Rosary Road and Barrack Street, below Ber Street and the city end of Earlham Road, the Pottergate area, and the Bracondale and Magdalen Road areas. Farther out of the city, there are known mine workings off Dereham Road, Newmarket Road and Ipswich Road. These areas are identified on Figure 115, but it is deliberate that no attempt has been made here to indicate the specific extent of any set of mine workings, which in any case would be too localised to show on a map at that scale.

In some cases (such as Earlham Road and Rosary Road) accurate plans do exist of workings (Figure 116) thanks to later surveying, but in most cases only isolated information has been recorded where tunnels have been exposed or their entrances found (Figure 117). There is always the likelihood that some tunnels have been forgotten after accesses have been blocked up or overgrown.

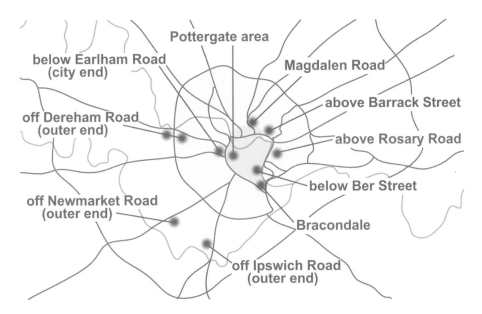

*Figure 115* Sketch map indicating general locations of some known chalk mines in Norwich. The red blobs have deliberately blurred edges to avoid any suggestion that the tunnel systems extend under the whole area covered by each blob.

*Figure 116* Northward aerial view of Thorpe Hamlet hillside in July 1932, with insets showing +11 m AOD. In the bottom right-hand corner is visible the corner of Norwich City's former ground,

## What hazard do they pose?

The mere existence of a tunnel in the chalk below a particular patch of ground does not necessarily mean there is a problem at the surface.

The hazards associated with underground voids are not unique to Norwich, and are reasonably well understood. Some historic tunnels have been deliberately filled in, while others are still standing open and thus pose a potential risk of collapse (Figure 118). Some seem to have been abandoned at the time of digging when they passed unexpectedly from chalk into natural zones of sand and the roof evidently caved in.

Where tunnels have been recorded or where there is considered a likelihood of them

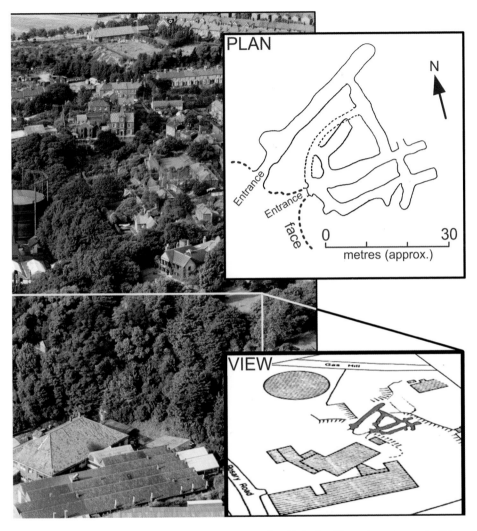

plan and location of tunnels converted into a wartime air raid shelter. These tunnels are at +9 to The Nest.

existing, these days no development would be permitted above them until detailed investigation had been completed and a properly engineered foundation system devised to cope with any future risks of collapse. In some cases, land has been left undeveloped and chalk mine accesses left open to provide a habitat for bats via a secure metal grill (Figure 119). Elsewhere, the way in has been deliberately closed off and/or hidden to deter subterranean explorers.

The most serious problems today occur when stability is disturbed by external factors, especially from construction works (Figure 120), or as a result of water leakage. These factors are implicated in most of the dramatic incidents of the recent past. It is no surprise

*Figure 117*
Left, tunnel
entrances off
Rosary Road
in the late
ninteenth
century in use
for storage of
beer, and
below,
the same
entrances in
2011, prior to
redevelopment
of the site for
flats

that recorded subsidence events often affect roads and buildings, because that is where water leakages are likely to occur and thus trigger ground movement.

The moral is to arrange for the ground to be properly checked before building in any of these susceptible areas, and as always, to aim to keep drains and other water services in good watertight condition (Figure 121). With this sensible and basic risk management, we can afford to relax a bit.

## Tunnels other than chalk mines

If tunnels are defined as underground passageways, then the chalk mines of Norwich are by no means the only tunnels. I have already mentioned myths about thoroughfares beneath the city, some of which undoubtedly do exist (such as the prisoners' tunnel at the Castle) but many of which may be fanciful (such as the link to St Benet's Abbey).

*Figure 118* Interior of tunnel off
Rosary Road, one of those shown in
Figure 117

*Figure 119* Secured entrance at
Eaton mines, off Newmarket Road at
around +16 m AOD, now an
important bat habitat

In the absence (so far) of any road or rail tunnels in the city, the main underground arteries are those carrying utility services. Here there is a fascinating story to be told about Norwich's hidden tunnelled sewers, which are real and very necessary for the modern city to operate.

In 1832 Norwich suffered a cholera outbreak, at a time when there was a mains water supply but there were only localised sewers, some of which were along the streets or open cockeys. After visits of government inspectors and much local discussion, an extensive sewerage scheme was proposed, and construction eventually commenced in 1869. After the original contractor gave up because of difficult ground conditions (including causing the loss of the tower of St Swithin's Church), construction was finally completed in 1871.

*Figure 120* Tunnel exposed during construction work in 1994 at the former Nest site off Rosary Road, some 3 m below pitch level. This set of tunnels is at a level of +12 to +15 m AOD. They do not connect to those shown in Figures 117 and 118.

*Figure 121 (below)* Evidence of long-term leakage from a domestic overflow pipe, a widespread problem affecting local authority-owned properties including in some subsidence-prone areas. Replacement of one washer here could greatly reduce the risk of foundation instability.

The scale of this project was impressive. It consisted of more than 16 km of main sewers ranging from 0.5 m diameter brick barrel pipes to 1.8 m by 1.2 m egg-shaped sewers mostly large enough to walk down. To add to the challenge of construction (this was before the days of compressed air), nearly 5 km of this sewer needed to be built *below* the water table, to allow the collected liquid sewage (which would otherwise have passed into the river) to drain by gravity all the way to a deep sump at Trowse at a level of -5 m AOD. The sewage was then pumped by steam engine back up the hill to Whitlingham Farm, downstream of the city, where it was discharged.

The 'low-level' sewer was constructed in an upstream (reverse) direction from Trowse via Bracondale, King Street and

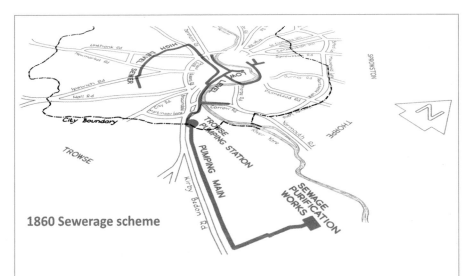

*Figure 122* Oblique map, viewed from the south-east side of Norwich, showing the layout of the first proper public sewerage scheme, completed in 1871. The low-level gravity sewer running beneath the line of Riverside Road, Rose Lane and King Street is nearly 3 km long.

Tombland to the council depot at Westwick Street, with a branch under the river along Carrow Road and another beneath the line of Rose Lane, Prince of Wales Road then under the river to Riverside Road (Figure 122). At its deepest point, below the highest ground at Bracondale, this sewer was more than 20 m below the surface, making for an interesting descent to the tunnel when accessed via the manholes there (Figure 123). There might have been a slightly more direct route from Carrow Bridge to Trowse below the Colman's Works site, but it seems that was avoided, probably on the orders of Jeremiah Colman to keep well clear of the deep abstraction wells that were about to be drilled on his factory site.

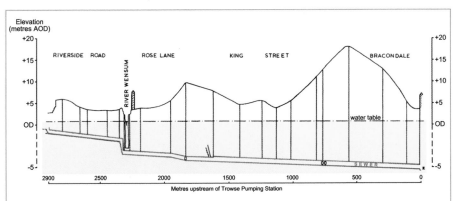

*Figure 123* Cross-section through the low-level sewer with greatly exaggerated vertical scale. This sewer was constructed entirely in saturated ground below the water table.

*Figure 124 (left)*
Pre-1960s view inside
the original brick-
lined low-level sewer,
showing leakage into
the sewer from the
surounding saturated
ground

*Figure 125 (below)*
1960s view during
refurbishment of the
sewer, involving lining
with concrete segments
and grouting behind to
seal it from the ground

Unfortunately the sub-water table sections of sewer proved insufficiently watertight, leaking groundwater *into* the completed sewer and thus overloading the sewage works (Figure 124). After various attempted repairs during the next 30 years, the low-level sewer was eventually abandoned and replaced with a higher-level sewer, using new technology which allowed the sewage to be moved in the necessary direction using compressed air generated at New Mills.

But the story did not end there. More than 60 years later, an expanding Norwich was again desperately in need of extra sewerage capacity, and with some effort, this old abandoned brick sewer was found, cleaned out, then lined with modern materials and thus brought back into use (Figure 125).

By this time (the late 1960s), the city's sewerage system had been greatly extended outwards, with a major route under development round the southern suburbs along the Yare Valley, and also a large

sewer serving Costessey and Hellesdon that came up the Wensum Valley to Barn Road. This latter concrete-lined sewer is 2.4 m in diameter, starts at river level with connections also from the city centre, and runs *downhill* for 3.4 km beneath the line of the inner ring road all the way to Trowse. It necessitated excavation of a large diameter tunnel in chalk using electric locomotives from below Grapes Hill onwards, reaching a depth of some 40 m below ground level at the top of Bracondale. The most difficult section was that running below Barn Road and Oak Street, just 'upstream' of Grapes Hill, requiring construction of a 1.7 m diameter sewer in wet sand, where temporary ground freezing proved necessary to allow the concrete pipes to be put in place.

Since that time, various smaller diameter tunnels have been constructed for drainage reasons, usually dug using hand-held equipment and lined with precast concrete segments. Examples are two sewers of about 1.5 m diameter installed in the 1980s, running from Unthank Road through to Westwick Street (passing beneath the Plantation Garden site), and from Chartwell Road to Oak Street (beneath Waterloo Park). They were designed to collect storm water from road gullies and take the flow in a direct line underground to new outfalls on the river (Figure 126), reducing the risk of flooding in the intervening residential areas. Needless to say, such storm sewers do nothing to reduce the potential of the river level to rise rapidly during storm conditions.

*Figure 126* Southward view across the River Wensum at the rear of Westwick Street showing the outfall (behind the timbers) of the storm sewer draining the Unthank Road area

*Figure 127* Damage to a gable wall, Magdalen Road, 1994

# Part IV

# When things sink

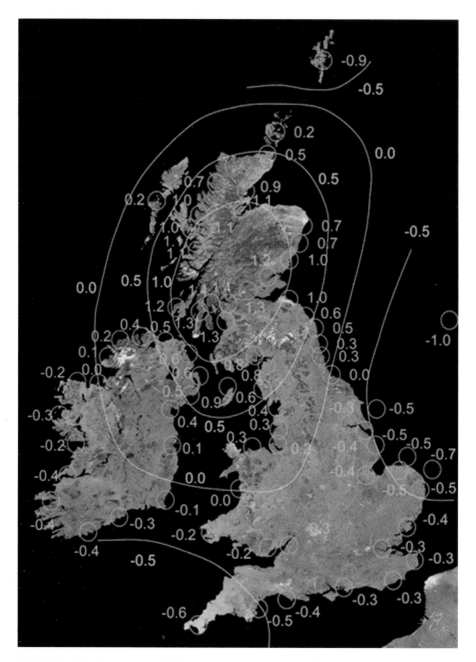

*Figure 128* Map showing land uplift (positive numbers) and subsidence (negative numbers) in mm per year, independent of any sea level rise

# 13
# Causes of ground movement

This section looks in a little more detail at the mechanisms through which some buildings in Norwich suffer from foundation-related damage. Understanding better why this can happen will help us to be more rational and less fearful if it does, and perhaps show us sensible steps we can take to reduce the risks of ground movement and building damage.

## The regional context

These days it is possible to monitor long-term ground movements over large geographical areas, and it has been established that there are significant variations in different parts of the United Kingdom (Figure 128). In essence, the north is very gradually rising up, and the country as a whole is tilting towards the east, so that in Norfolk we are indeed gradually sinking. The reasons for the movement are to do with the earth's crust's reaction to changing stresses including tectonic movements and (in the case of Scotland) the release of the weight of a thick covering of ice a few thousand years ago.

These slow movements occurring over a period of many centuries are usually expressed in millimetres per year. Norwich lies within a region where the ongoing sinking is thought to average around 0.5 mm per year, compared with a rise in central Scotland in the order of 1.5 mm per year.

The coastal effects of the regional movement are complicated by progressive global sea level rise, which is happening for climatic reasons. This averaged about 6mm per year over the past 20,000 years as the planet emerged from glaciation, had reduced to around 1.5 mm per year a century ago, and is now estimated to be running at around 3.5 mm per year for reasons that are well publicised and largely human-induced.

## Ground movement and damage

If a whole region or even a whole street sinks into the ground by the same amount at the same time, then you would not necessarily notice it, because buildings would all still appear at the same level in relation to one another. Of course, you might well notice the movement as you crossed a boundary into the affected area if this took the form of a step down that was not there before, or if there was a large crack in the pavement.

The point is that for damage to buildings and infrastructure to occur, the movement has to be *differential*. That is, it must affect only part of the structure, or occur at a rate or magnitude that varies strongly along the line of a wall (Figure 129). It is this differential component that is the cause of cracking of brick-and-mortar walls and similar structures that are relatively brittle. Other construction such as timber or plastic framing, or articulated brick paving, will to some extent deform by bending rather than cracking, and that might be by deliberate design. However, there are other consequences to consider, such as in the case of underground drainage pipes, which might (if made of plastic) survive differential ground movement but end up sloping in the wrong direction for flow, leading to ponding or blockage.

*Figure 129* Differential movement has caused cracking of a flint wall, St Andrew's Hall, 2012. The damage is now hidden behind a permanent sign board!

## Is Norwich uniquely affected?

Even when Norwich is not being described as 'riddled with tunnels', the city is sometimes portrayed as affected by widespread subsidence problems. The question is whether there are subterranean aspects that put buildings at greater risk in Norwich than elsewhere.

It is true that unlike many cities in the central and northern parts of the United Kingdom, Norwich cannot boast the presence of solid rock at shallow depths. This geological situation would allow tall buildings to be constructed off shallow foundations with little risk of movement. The city lies in a 'soft rock' area where the potential founding strata are often gravelly sands, weathered chalk or occasionally sandy clays. These soil types are prone to more squashing under load than, say, sandstone or limestone (Figure 130).

Another factor often overlooked is the sheer intensity of urban activity in a city with such a long and busy history. For many centuries there has been digging and delving, washing and draining, and all sorts of other disturbance – but with constant reliance on the integrity of the ground. This inevitably ends up putting to the test any zones that are prone to ground movement.

When buildings show signs of distress, it is in theory possible to classify the level of damage based on the measured width of the cracks, ranging from less than 1mm (classified as 'very slight' damage) through to more than 25mm ('very severe'). This then informs the need for further monitoring to see whether the movement has stopped or whether things are getting worse.

The expectation of what is 'normal' in buildings and the perception of what constitutes 'a problem' is rather subjective among different owners. Someone moving to Norwich

Box 3

*Settlement versus subsidence*

If you are a property owner and have an insurance policy, it is as well to know the difference between 'settlement' and 'subsidence', a distinction that might appear in your policy wording.

'**Settlement**' is regarded as movement that is caused by the distribution (or redistribution) of the building loads during the early stages of the building's life, or what might be thought of as 'settling down' or 'bedding down'.

'**Subsidence**', on the other hand, occurs when the ground beneath the building is unable to support it, and this can happen at any stage in the building's life, in many cases unrelated to when the foundation loading was applied.

This distinction allows insurers to avoid being responsible for making good minor cracks which commonly affect new buildings in the first few months (or even years) following construction, but provides cover (beyond the policy excess) for dealing with more serious or progressive damage if that occurs later on.

However, from a technical viewpoint it is difficult to make a clear distinction between settlement and subsidence, because it is largely a matter of timing. It is true that some 'settlement' movement of foundations usually occurs before the bearing resistance of the soil has fully developed, but the time taken for this to happen varies enormously depending on the soil type (potentially anything from minutes to decades) and on the stage at which the weight of the building or its contents is actually applied to the soil in relation to the construction sequence. There is no universal acceptance of the length of time beyond which 'bedding down' movements are no longer tolerable, and in reality many buildings are subject to alterations, extensions and changes of use over time. Furthermore there is often a two-way reaction between the behaviour of the building and that of the ground. For example the soil might 'give' a bit, the building sink a little, then the soil give a bit more.

from the Fens (where tilted buildings are not unusual) might not even notice a leaning wall in a 1930s bungalow in Costessey, whereas the Londoner purchasing a brand new executive home in Eaton might be aghast at discovering a hairline crack in the plaster beneath a window sill. Box 3 explains the difference between settlement and subsidence.

## The influence of the Norwich chalk

We have seen from the rational 4D model that the whole of the city is underlain by chalk, albeit at a depth below the present ground surface that varies greatly in different localities. It is true to say that the chalk has certain characteristics that have contributed to Norwich's reputation as a location where there is less than solid ground to build on.

How strong is the chalk beneath the city? The fact that it can form the unsupported roof to a tunnel (Figure 131) suggests that it is 'firm', but in comparison with other rock-types (or indeed with the chalk of Flamborough Head or the Needles) we could qualify

*Figure 130* Houses at Park Lane: were those window sills built like that? No, but houses can settle after construction.

that to 'firm*ish*'. Certainly it is not hard for it to be readily dug out of the ground with a pick and shovel to create a tunnel. Indeed, the Norwich chalk gets a bad press because it is often only seen on building sites as munched-up spoil recovered from a drilling machine or piling rig. In this condition it is a sticky white material with the consistency of porridge (Figure 132). The reason is that chalk is almost entirely composed of billions of tiny granules of calcium carbonate which are actually the fossil shells of microscopic organisms. These are hollow and filled with water which is readily released when the chalk is disturbed, hence the stodgy mess. This is not necessarily a reflection of its normal state at depth. Box 4 explains what we know about flints in the chalk.

A second characteristic of the chalk in Norwich is that it is usually covered over by a layer of a different material, as shown on the cross-section and rational model (Figure 14, page 14). More often than not, these 'cover deposits' consist of sand, and it is the inter-

*Figure 131* Close-up of the roof of the chalk tunnel at Harford Hills. This has stood for at least a century since the mine was first dug.

*Figure 132* Sticky 'porridge' chalk being cleared from the auger of a piling rig in Pottergate, 2011

Box 4

## What is flint?

Flint is one of the few hard building materials available in Norfolk. It is a form of silica found as nodules in the chalk, as well as in other deposits derived from it when it is eroded. Because flint has no simple crystalline structure, it splinters or breaks with a cone-shaped fracture (like glass). This attribute was exploited by Stone Age people who made flint tools with sharp cutting edges.

There is much debate on exactly how and at what stage flints formed

*Figure 133* Painting of a paramoudra taken from the chalk pit at Caistor St Edmund. The hole down the middle is about 200 mm across.

in the chalk, but it is generally thought this happened some time after the chalk mud accumulated. The silica was initially a saturated 'gel' that was precipitated in the presence of certain chemicals, including the amino acids of living beings. This might explain the Norfolk phenomenon of 'paramoudras', which are vertical columns of large hollow flints (each about the size of a toilet bowl) which it is thought might have formed around the deep burrows of worms on the chalk sea floor (Figure 133).

*Figure 134* St Lawrence's Church, a massive medieval structure built on a platform cut into a steep slope formed of chalk. The fall in level from St Benedict's to Westwick Street is about 6 m.

action of the sand and underlying chalk that has led to many of the reported foundation problems in the city. That is why old buildings built directly upon undisturbed chalk where it occurs naturally at a shallow depth (Figure 134) are generally regarded as having more reliable foundations than those built on higher ground where there is a significant covering of sand.

A third characteristic is that chalk has a tendency to acquire holes. We have already considered (in Part III) those voids that are human-made: in other words, chalk workings that might be horizontal (tunnels/adits) or vertical (shafts/wells). However, there can also be holes of natural origin, in which case they go under the general name of natural solution features. See Box 5 for an explanation of how natural solution features work.

It is the above three characteristics acting in combination that have been implicated in most of the more dramatic subsidence events in Norwich. Holes unexpectedly opening up in the ground are usually the last stage in a process whereby cover deposits have been migrating downwards into voids in the chalk, usually washed down by percolating water.

In many cases a certain amount of ground investigation is needed before it can be established

*Figure 135* Severe subsidence affecting a terraced house in Finkelgate, late December 2010. The end house was subsequently demolished.

Box 5

## Natural solution features

The word 'solution' here refers to the process of dissolution, because a solution feature begins with the opening out of natural joints (cracks) in the chalk by the reaction of the calcium carbonate with slightly acidic water that has percolated down through the overlying sandy layers. The joints in the top of the chalk become enlarged and form fissures, and these are gradually filled with sand particles that have been washed down from above (Figure 136). It is thought this can be either a sudden or a geologically slow process, depending on the drainage conditions. Pipes of sand (or 'sand pots') extending to an unknown depth have quite often been found when the upper part of the chalk is exposed in excavations, or intercepted during tunnelling operations.

These sand-filled fissures tend to become preferred drainage pathways for percolating water, and so the process can continue over a long period, with progressive enlargement of the fissures and downward movement of sand, so that a zone of loosened sand develops above the feature. The whole process is driven by water, so what might take say tens of years during normal climatic conditions can occur over hours if there is a burst water main or major drain leak. Uneven slumping of the sand at depth can result in cavities forming. When these do eventually collapse, the overall effect is that the cavities migrate upwards (in other words, they swap places with the overlying sand) until they finally pop out at the ground surface. This has a potentially unexpected and serious effect on building foundations or on paved areas.

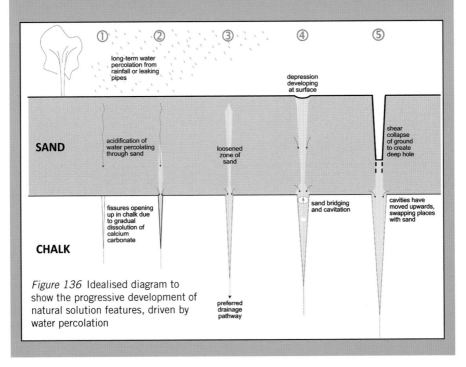

*Figure 136* Idealised diagram to show the progressive development of natural solution features, driven by water percolation

Attempts have been made to predict the incidence of solution features as they affect the chalk outcrop across the United Kingdom using statistical methods, but it seems that the reported frequency (measured as, say, the number of features per square kilometre) might be strongly influenced by the intensity of

Figure 137
Ground collapse affecting the rear corner of the Beeches Hotel, off Earlham Road, April 2016

land use. Where collapses occur in agricultural areas, they are less likely to be recorded, whereas in an urban area like Norwich, every collapse (whatever the cause) is likely to be noticed (Figure 137).

A theoretically ideal way to assess the degree of risk in Norwich is to slice off the ground near the top of the chalk and determine directly the frequency of visible sand-

Figure 138 Castle Mall under construction: view towards Golden Ball Street in late February 1992

filled fissures or pipes in the chalk by simply counting them. This is hardly practical in the normal scheme of things. However we did have that opportunity in the city centre in 1991–92 when a large excavation down to the chalk was made for the Castle Mall shopping centre. At the time, it was expected that the floor of the 'quarry' (which was taken down to a reduced level of around +8 m AOD) would be entirely white chalk, but it turned out that some 10 per cent of the area consisted of sand-filled solution features (Figure 139). These ranged in size from less than 1 m across up to 20 m across, and they were roughly 20 m apart. Rather alarmingly, they were not always vertical-sided in form, sometimes getting larger with depth. Their presence led to the need for expensive additional engineering measures during construction of the foundations to the shopping centre (Figure 138).

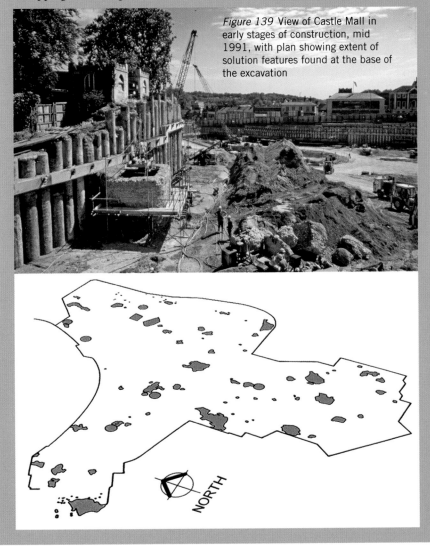

*Figure 139* View of Castle Mall in early stages of construction, mid 1991, with plan showing extent of solution features found at the base of the excavation

whether the underground void at depth is (or was) natural or human in origin, as the effects at the surface of ground collapse might look identical (Figure 135). It is not unusual for voiding to occur owing to a combination of human and natural causes (such as where a tunnel intercepts a 'sand pot' leading to a collapse at the surface). Similarly, it is often unclear at the outset whether the water percolation is attributable to natural drainage or to a specific human-made source, such as a leaking drain or water main. Drain runs can themselves be damaged by ground movement, so we are sometimes dealing with a chicken-and-egg situation which can lead to much wrangling between owners and insurers over who exactly is responsible.

## Causes of subsidence not involving chalk

We have seen that the more dramatic instances of subsidence in Norwich which have helped to give it its reputation are usually linked to the characteristics of the local chalk. The city still nevertheless manages to display the usual range of ground problems associated with any historic urban area.

These include the effects of past resculpting of the ground (described in Part II), involving both ground level raising (filling), and the modification of slopes by quarrying. Where low-lying flood plain areas have been raised by filling and subsequently built on, there might be long-term gradual movement of building foundations owing to consolidation of the added soil or underlying soft natural deposits, or perhaps by gradual breakdown of the organic constituents in the soil as they oxidise and decompose. The magnitude of these effects is usually greatest during the years directly following filling, but the process can continue over many decades. Walls only crack when the movements are differential – which could happen because of varying building loads, lateral changes in the strength or thickness of the compressible soil, or the presence of old foundations causing 'hard spots' over which a later building could 'break its back'.

When the Duke of Norfolk's men started to build his three-storey palace (Figure 140) on a riverside site north of St Andrew's Street in 1561, they first had to reclaim what was previously a low-lying flood plain (at around +1 m AOD) bounded by the Great Cockey. Archaeological work has shown that there was deliberate and extensive ground level raising ahead of construction, with a layer of chalk (Figure 141) placed above the natural marsh deposits, then other soil built up to provide the necessary platform on which to place the large building (at a level of around +4 m AOD). The combination of these soft deposits, loose fill and a heavy building sounds like a recipe for long-term foundation movements, and we can indeed find some clues to such problems in succeeding

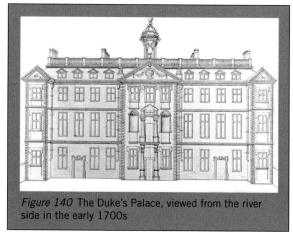

*Figure 140* The Duke's Palace, viewed from the river side in the early 1700s

accounts. When Thomas Baskerville visited in 1681 he described the building as 'not yet finished within' and 'seated in a dung-hole place'. In its later years the palace apparently fell into dereliction, and in 1739 there is a report of three children dying when a wall fell on them. The 'official' reason for the then Duke to vacate the palace and leave Norwich in 1711 was his annoyance at having been refused a processional entry by the Lord Mayor, who was evidently worried about

*Figure 141*
Archaeological excavation at the Duke's Palace site, February 2003, showing a layer of chalk resting on marsh deposits covered by a further 3 m of raised ground

pro-Catholic rioting. However, he might already have had strong reasons for getting out because the palace had become uninhabitable following subsidence. We know some of it was demolished soon afterwards.

Subsidence caused by **unstable slopes** is normally associated with hilly cities, and we have seen that Norwich does have some steep gradients. The risks increase when these slopes have been subjected to quarrying, and that is the case in certain parts of the city where the extraction of chalk from the valley sides has left some faces considerably steeper than the natural condition. One such area is above Rosary Road below Thorpe Hamlet (Figure 116, page 100), where much of the quarried slope is now wooded. While the trees can cling on and remain in place, the stability is helped by the network of roots, but loss of vegetation or new construction works can occasionally lead to slope collapse.

As we have seen, the former Norwich City Football Club ground at The Nest was situated in a partly backfilled former chalk pit, and the former steep faces on the uphill side were supported by large concrete retaining walls built in 1908 (Figure 142). These included some spectator terracing. The proximity of the walls to the pitch was one of the reasons the ground was considered substandard when the club achieved promotion to the Second Division in 1935, and a decision was made to build a new ground at Carrow Road. In retrospect, given the unstable ground in the area and the large number of spectators who packed into The Nest, it is only good fortune that in

*Figure 142* Original concrete retaining wall under construction at The Nest football ground, off Rosary Road, in 1908

27 years there was not a major accident. The cracked concrete retaining walls (complete with original painted advertising slogans) survived to the 1990s, when the site was occupied by a book warehouse. During works to construct an extension close to one of the walls, part of the slope suddenly collapsed, bringing down a mass of sandy soil which had previously supported part of the garden to a house in Malvern Road (Figure 143). The damage was considerable, but luckily no one was hurt. The slope was later stabilised ahead of residential redevelopment (Figure 144).

Publications on subsidence frequently cite seasonal **heave and shrinkage** of clay subsoil as the most significant risk to house foundations. This is perhaps a rather London-centric outlook, and it is true that many parts of south-east England are affected, especially in proximity to trees, because the root network can extend the zone affected by drying-out of the soil during droughts. The sandy clay soils in Norfolk are generally of glacial origin (known as glacial till) and are much less shrinkable than the marine-deposited clays found elsewhere (such as London clay). In Norwich itself about the only clay found is brick-earth (a sandy clay similar to glacial till), which is not particularly prone to heave and shrinkage. Where trees are sometimes implicated in ground movements affecting walls, it is often the physical displacement of soil by the roots that is the issue, rather than volume change of the soil caused by moisture changes.

**Traffic vibration** is sometimes blamed for the cracking of buildings, but this effect is usually over-rated, and visible damage to walls can often be attributed to other causes. Humans are rather more sensitive to vibration than are buildings.

*Figure 143* Collapse of the slope at the former Nest during construction of a replacement retaining wall during warehouse extensions in 1994, with parts of the original wall propped

*Figure 144* The stabilised slope to the rear of the Scholars' Quarter housing development off Rosary Road, constructed from 2007, photographed in 2016

## Investigation of the ground

These days there are many different physical techniques available for investigating what is going on below a particular patch of ground – including excavating, boring or probing. There are also a range of high-tech geophysical methods that usually require trusting skilled operators to coax meaningful results out of the data input. As we will usually only ever be able to explore a tiny percentage of the ground, it is always worth taking stock before rushing in blind and attempting what can often be a costly exploratory exercise.

As we have seen, having a rational model of the expected ground conditions, based on the known relative levels and the historic context, can usually get investigators a good way along the path of understanding before they even set foot on the site, effectively giving them a hypothesis (or ground model) which an investigation can then test. Deciding what they are trying to achieve should help them to choose the most appropriate method, perhaps targeting particular bits of required information (such as the depth to the chalk or the nature of the soil immediately below foundation level). This avoids the expenditure of time and effort in gathering large amounts of irrelevant or unnecessary data.

Often in a built-up area, the choice of method of investigation is strongly influenced by the space available to work in, not least if there are buildings in the way. Unsurprisingly this is usually the case when the aim is to establish why a building is cracking up. It may therefore be appropriate to use a lightweight 'imaging' method (such as small diameter probing, Figure 145), at a place very close to the building and also at a more distant location, to determine how conditions compare between the two. The next stage is to carry out more rigorous soil sampling or testing (such as from a larger diameter borehole) at the more distant location where there is sufficient space to set up the drilling equipment.

There is no substitute for direct inspection of the soil. It is always desirable to make some sort of hole in the ground by digging, probing or boring (known as 'intrusive' investigation) in order to view and sample the soil, but this is not always practical. Where conditions allow, non-intrusive methods such as geophysical investigation or remote sensing can be useful

Figure 145 A selection of small probing rigs testing deeply filled ground ahead of construction of retirement housing off Earlham Road, photographed from the footbridge over Grapes Hill in November 2004

in detecting features or anomalies, but these still usually have to be proved by subsequent direct investigation.

In broad terms, the more sophisticated and specialised a particular exploratory method, the less able it is to deal with conditions that depart from those expected. In Norwich, that could for example mean the unanticipated presence of coarse gravel which obstructs or damages the delicate tip of a high-tech probe, or the presence of underground cables or other services that mask or scramble geophysical data gathered at the ground surface. For that reason, it is often best to opt for the simplest and least vulnerable exploratory method unless there is a good reason to choose otherwise. This explains the survival of the traditional 'cable percussion' drilling technique in UK site investigation. This 'belt and braces' method of making a 150 mm diameter borehole in the ground (originally developed for well drilling) has continued to be the mainstay of the site investigation industry (Figure 146). Provided there is space to set up the drilling rig, cable percussion can usually cope with whatever it encounters in Norwich, from soft cheese to cannon-shot gravel, and recover samples from a known depth to look at.

## Subsidence cause and effect

We have looked at possible causes of ground movement in Norwich, but establishing the precise mechanism for a given case of subsidence it not always a straightforward task.

Because of the costs of investigation, the process of determining what has happened is usually funded by a party who has a strong financial interest in the outcome: an insurance company or the property owner, or some cases another party pursuing litigation.

Insurers and lawyers understandably want to prove a straightforward cause-and-effect relationship between what has happened in the ground and the damage sustained by the building or other structure. This enables them to identify what (or who) is to blame and allocate the costs of rectifying the problem accordingly. For example, it might be shown that a water main leaked, washing away the soil, and the foundation subsequently moved. Factor A caused consequence B (see Figure 147), and in this case the party responsible for the water main is presumably liable. Unfortunately, this approach to analysis of the physical problem is not necessarily the same as a scientific approach, which recognises that there is often a two-way interaction between various elements including the soil, foundations, water and other external factors, over a variable timescale, and is more interested in understanding the whole system than in ascribing blame or legal liability.

Figure 146 A cable percussion drilling rig carrying out ground investigation on a site at St Martin's Lane, October 2001

This more scientific approach, which can equally be applied to – for example – analysing road traffic incidents, is sometimes described as the 'three Cs'. That acronym stands for 'critical combination of circumstances', and it recognises that there are usually three or more factors involved in the incident (in this context, subsidence), and that the event has happened because the factors just happened to come together (see Figure 148).

For example, the three factors could be an overflowing gutter, a localised zone of loosely infilled ground, and a weakly constructed foundation beneath the wall. Take away any one of the factors and the cracking would not have occurred, but that does not mean that this factor is wholly to blame. It took all three things happening together. So the weak footing managed to support the wall crossing the zone of loose ground for a number of years, but one day it failed because it had been inundated with water spilling from the gutter. Normally a footing should be strong enough not to fail if crossing weaker ground,

Figure 147 A simple cause and effect model as preferred by insurers and lawyers. In this case, factor A might be a water leak and consequence B might be a wall subsiding.

Figure 148
A more
sophisticated
model recognising
multiple factors
coming together.
Water is usually
one of the factors
involved in
subsidence in
Norwich; the
others could be
weak foundations
and structural
loading.

**C**ritical

**C**ombination

of **C**ircumstances

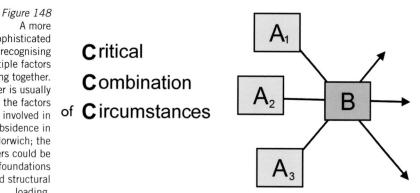

a bit of surface water shouldn't cause a wall to crack, and most buildings suffer occasional gutter overflows, especially in the autumn. The damage was the result of the three factors coming together.

The three Cs approach does not necessarily mean that all factors are given equal weight, however. If the property owner had been aware of the weak foundation they could perhaps have taken more precautions, such as being extra vigilant to avoid the gutter being left for months blocked with leaves.

Another way in which the traditional cause-and-effect approach is problematic is that factors sometimes extend beyond property boundaries. This is especially true in the case of terraced or semi-detached houses, when water leakage in one part of a block can lead to cracking elsewhere, and stabilisation of foundations to one unit can over time cause renewed differential movement and cracking if the foundations of other units in the block are not also stabilised at the same time (Figure 149).

Figure 149 A single terraced house, such as this example at Gertrude Road, may have to be treated as part of a larger structure when it comes to implementing foundation improvements

# 14
## Managing risk

Now that you have acquired a rational model for understanding ground conditions, you should be in a better position to decide what precautions it is sensible to take to help protect property from the damaging effects of ground movement. Usually this refers to buildings, but it applies to anything in contact with the ground, whether it is something permanent needing foundations, retaining walls, underground services or paving, or something more portable resting on the surface such as a heavy vehicle, sculpture or shed.

Risk assessment is outlined in Box 6. The measures that can be taken differ to some extent between *existing* property (which is likely to concern most home owners) and the construction of *new* buildings (the typical situation for builders and developers).

## Risk management for existing property

Many of the mechanisms for ground movement in Norwich involve water percolation as a key factor. Often the arrival of water triggers movement when there are other pre-existing risk factors. It follows that the most effective risk management for owners is likely to involve taking practical steps to reduce the probability of water getting into the ground in the vicinity of foundations and similar structures. For most householders this need not mean anything more complicated than making sure that gutters and downpipes are cleared regularly of leaves (Figure 150) and that drain gullies are kept unblocked. If you notice other water-related problems such as suspected leaks, overflows or surface ponding affecting the building, you will probably want to call in a specialist such as a plumber or builder. The same applies if you suspect that underground drain runs are defective, especially in the close vicinity of load-bearing walls.

*Figure 150* Water overflowing from a gutter blocked with leaves runs straight down onto the wall foundations

## Risk management for new buildings

A number of attempts have been made to produce national or regional maps of ground-related hazards using statistical methods, and these are potentially useful for large-scale

Box 6

*Understanding risk*

Risk assessment is a well-developed topic in these risk-averse days. It is applied to a wide range of situations, such as the planning of a school or the design of a nuclear power station, as well as smaller issues such as deciding whether to buy a house. From a rational viewpoint, it is generally accepted that the **risk** of something happening depends on two independent factors: the **probability** of that event happening, and the **consequences** should it happen. This is usually represented by the mathematical formula

Risk ($R$) = Probability ($P$) x Consequences ($C$)

More sophisticated risk assessment approaches attach precise numerical figures to these entities and then look mathematically at the results of applying safety measures. But this simple formula is still useful when we apply it in a non-numerical or qualitative way. This gives rise to a 'risk matrix' (see Figure 151) which can be used to help justify risk management decisions on paper.

For example, let's take the situation of managing (in other words reducing) the risk $R$ associated with the walls of a new building developing cracks. That can be done by reducing the probability $P$ of ground movement, or reducing the consequences $C$ of that movement, or both. The best solution might be to consolidate the ground before building, to reduce $P$, and use flexible timber framed construction, to reduce $C$.

It is important to note that this risk formula is not capable of producing zero risk $R$, because there will always be positive factors $P$ and $C$, however small. That fact need not alarm us, as it is true of all aspects of our daily life – which are always associated with variable degrees of risk. Whether we know it or not, we instinctively do much to manage immediate and short-term risks according to our own personal 'risk thermostat', which is set fairly low in most people, but is never zero or we would not get out of bed in the morning. In the case of buildings, decisions are generally made for the long term, on behalf of users, owners and even future generations.

CONSEQUENCES OF SUBSIDENCE →

| PROBABILITY OF SUBSIDENCE ↑ | Negligible | Minor | Moderate | Significant | Severe |
|---|---|---|---|---|---|
| Very likely | LOW MEDIUM | MEDIUM | MEDIUM HIGH | HIGH | HIGH |
| Likely | LOW | LOW MEDIUM | MEDIUM | MEDIUM HIGH | HIGH |
| Possible | LOW | LOW MEDIUM | MEDIUM | MEDIUM HIGH | MEDIUM HIGH |
| Unlikely | LOW | LOW MEDIUM | LOW MEDIUM | MEDIUM | MEDIUM HIGH |
| Very unlikely | LOW | LOW | LOW MEDIUM | MEDIUM | MEDIUM |

*Figure 151* A typical 'risk matrix' used to get a non-numerical estimate of the risks of subsidence, depending on which combination of probability and consequences is chosen

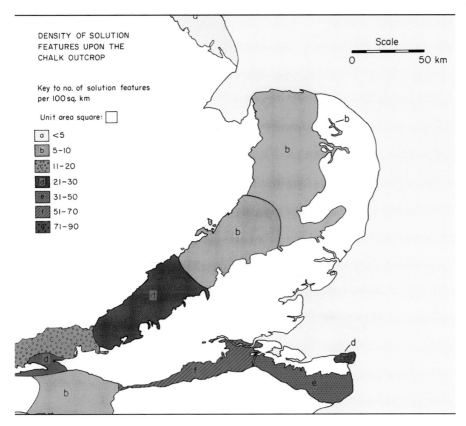

DENSITY OF SOLUTION
FEATURES UPON THE
CHALK OUTCROP

Key to no. of solution features
per 100 sq. km

Unit area square: ☐

| a | <5 |
| b | 5-10 |
| c | 11-20 |
| d | 21-30 |
| e | 31-50 |
| f | 51-70 |
| g | 71-90 |

Scale

0                  50 km

*Figure 152* Part of a hazard map showing the density of solution features on the chalk outcrop in
East Anglia

planning (an example is Figure 152). These are the sorts of approach used by large
insurance companies to assess risk and set premiums. General conclusions may be drawn
about the risks of building in the Norwich area, but the resolution of the data on which
hazard maps are based is unlikely to be sufficient to define where problems exist on a
particular site, so this is never an adequate substitute for site-specific investigation.

Many of the obvious water-related risks are recognised in national building regulations
relating to pipe construction and drainage. A general aim today is also to produce more
sustainable drainage systems, which are designed to return rainwater to the ground rather
than piping it straight to a river outfall. In Norwich's generally permeable ground conditions, which are vulnerable to the effects of water percolation, this presents a challenge in
higher density developments, because it can increase the danger of washing away the soil
near foundations and triggering subsidence (Figure 153).

New soakaways should preferably be positioned well away (a standard minimum is
5 m) from new foundations, and be as numerous and dispersed as practicable. It is also
best if they are positioned below future planted areas rather than paved surfaces in order
to minimise the consequences of localised subsidence, which can never altogether be

*Figure 153 Left,* partial collapse of large soakaway built beneath a car park at a city school, caused by concentrated water flow triggering a solution feature, *below,* in August 2008

ruled out. New retaining walls must be designed with good drainage behind them to avoid build-up of water, with a robust means of ensuring that the drains continue to function for years to come.

In cases where site investigation has identified particular hazards in the ground (such as possible voids or soft zones), the new build process provides the opportunity to engineer things in such a way as to either greatly reduce the hazard, or altogether avoid it (Figure 154). This can involve extending foundations laterally or downward, using reinforced concrete, steel or even timber, pumping grout or resin into the ground, or consolidating it using a large vibrating poker. Considerable ingenuity has been applied in devising a range of proprietary solutions, and the choice will often depend not just on the ground conditions, but also the size of the job, the access space and vulnerability of nearby structures. Figures 155 to 158 give some Norwich examples.

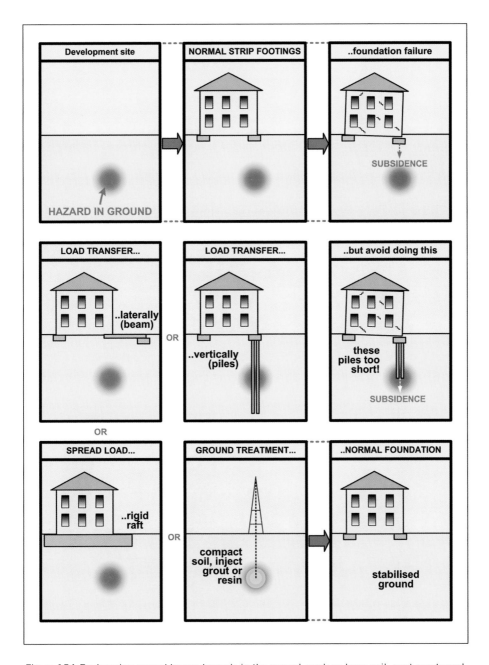

*Figure 154* Engineering around known hazards in the ground, such as loose soil, peat or a tunnel

*Figure 155* Auger piles being installed through archaeological layers for new houses on a site at Blackfriars Street off Fishergate, March 2014

*Figure 156* Specialist ground improvement over a grid of compaction points on a deeply filled site at Chalk Hill House in 1990. A suspended poker is vibrated into loose ground then gravel tipped and compacted into the holes formed to form a series of stone columns to 'reinforce' the ground.

ERECTING NEW BRIDGE, HEIGHAM FERRY, NORWICH. MARCH 3RD 1909
(PIONEER SERIES)

*Figure 157* Concrete piles being driven through peat in 1909 to support the new footbridge over the river taking the Dolphin Path from Heigham Street towards Drayton Road

*Figure 158* Resin injection in progress at Grove Road 2012, for the foundation for a new stairwell in an area of backfilled brick workings. The illustration on the lorry shows what is ideally happening below ground.

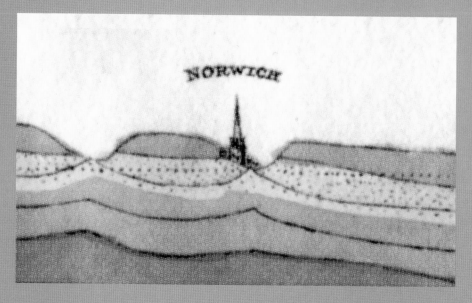

*Figure 159* Extract from a geological cross-section of Norfolk by Samuel Woodward, 1833. (It was his grandson Horace B. Woodward who would go on to be responsible for the first official geological survey of the Norwich district in 1881.)

# Part V

# Geology drives everything

*Figure 160* Cut made through buildings in 1899 to make a link for the trams between Bank Plain and St Andrew's Plain, leaving us the steep hill past Cinema City

*Figure 161* Cleveland Road runs down the gradient into the city centre from the Grapes Hill roundabout, slicing diagonally across property boundaries and breaking through the original St Giles Street frontage next to Churchman House

# 15
# The grain of the city

## Interpreting the landscape

This account of subterranean Norwich could have been subtitled 'an understanding of the city from ground level downwards'. So now you have reached this point in this account, I hope you have a reasonable grasp of what is beneath our feet in the city and how it relates to what we see at the surface.

I have done this by trying to build up a rational four-dimensional model, one that can always be further refined and modified as more information comes to light. The model-making benefits greatly if we aim to think in terms of *relative* levels (in relation to a fixed datum rather than merely depth below ground), and it also helps if we make use of some basic geological and physical principles.

The model can and should be informed by our casual observations and experiences as we make our way around Norwich and the surrounding area. Why is this area so low-lying? Why is there a sudden change of levels over there? Could that ground be filled? Are we passing onto the chalk slope? It is thus possible to start 'reading the landscape'.

For me personally one of the best tools for 'interpreting the landscape' is my bicycle, whether this is a conscious process or otherwise. Cycling is a great way of understanding (and physically experiencing) gradients that you might otherwise not notice on foot or using motorised transport. This is certainly true out in the Norfolk countryside, where the gradients are often subtle and the causes not always obvious.

The very best time to read the landscape is in spring, before the leaves come on the trees and while the sun is still low in the sky, adding the full visual experience to that felt through the pedalling. The constantly changing visual perspective as you move across the surface enables the brain to build up and internalise a subtle three-dimensional model of the shape of the land.

In an intensely historic (and relatively hilly) place like Norwich, you soon get to be able to distinguish the medieval streets from the Victorian and later additions because of their lack of steep gradients. If a medieval cart could be rolled up a slope, you can be sure it is reasonably comfortable cycling, and most of the medieval street pattern tends to follow the contours – our medieval ancestors knew how to work with the natural landscape. On the other hand, a sudden steep climb across the gradients is often a sign of a later addition to the street network, be it a late Victorian cut-through to create a tram route (Figure 160), or a mid-twentieth century link road for motor vehicles (Figure 161).

When leaving the city centre at Bishop Bridge and heading for Thorpe St Andrew, a bicycle rider has a choice between the shortest route straight ahead, a precipitous climb up the 'river cliff' known as Gas Hill, and at the other extreme, a near-flat route to the right alongside the meandering river all the way round to Carrow and ultimately to Thorpe, albeit rather a major detour. This is probably much the choice originally faced by the medieval carter (Gas Hill being an ancient walking route). The solution is the compromise route, half rightward and up over the shoulder of the hill at an acceptable gradient (Figure 162). These days it is called Rosary Road, but it appears on old maps,

*Figure 162* Panoramic composite view eastwards to southwards from Bishop Bridge showing the choice of route between Gas Hill (left) and Rosary Road (right)

including in the background of Cunningham's Prospect of 1558 (Figure 163). We also know this is an old road because it survived when quarrying was taking place on both the uphill and downhill sides of it, and tunnels were constructed to pass beneath it. It is no surprise that Rosary Road is a preferred route for cyclists in both directions.

Also visible on Cunningham's Prospect is a large area of city centre land south-east of the Cathedral shown as open meadows and not built on. Our rational model immediately tells us why this land remained undeveloped for so long – it is of course the wide natural flood plain to the River Wensum, underlain by soft organic river deposits and a shallow water table. It was necessary to cross this marshy area to access Bishop Bridge, but that was achieved by means of a raised causeway (Holme Street) which is now Bishopgate. We may be grateful the marsh was not entirely filled and built over, as happened elsewhere.

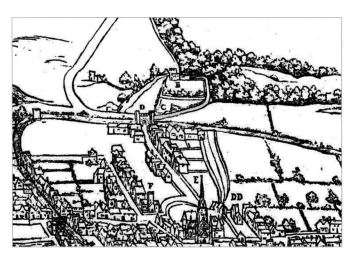

*Figure 163* Extract from William Cunningham's prospect of Norwich of 1558, eastward view over Bishopgate to Rosary Road (highlighted in yellow)

## What is meant by the 'grain' of the city?

It should become obvious that there is, in geographical terms, a linear relationship between the natural geology of the city, which determines its topography and drainage, and the way the city has developed over the centuries. This has strongly influenced things like the street layout, the parish boundaries, where quarrying has happened, and some of these things have been modified by human beings as we have gone along. It can be argued that geology has profoundly affected what the inhabitants have done, the way they have behaved, and this has essentially left us our city heritage. This can be represented diagrammatically as a linkage from Geology through to Heritage (Figure 164).

Another way of looking at it is that there is a natural 'grain' to the city (that is, what is dictated by its geological setting). The city has evolved in accordance with that grain, give or take some human interventions along the way.

I have already mentioned (on pages 52–3) examples of historic city streets positioned along the edges of the original flood plains, which evolved from trackways carefully skirting the soft muddy areas. These roads preserve the 'grain' of the valley floor even though most of the flood plains have now disappeared beneath fill. There are plenty of other examples of geological or topographical 'grain' fossilised into historic features, such as parish boundaries that follow lost watercourses (for example, Figure 165).

It is self-evident that the location of the former quarried areas is closely related to the sub-crop of particular geological layers, but we can extend this idea to recognise how geology has profoundly influenced the shape of the landscape, the topography. This is one of the key factors that has dictated the layout of Norwich's roads and streets. It is also interesting to consider the influence of topography on the original choice of the shape of the defended medieval core. The city wall, which forms about two-thirds of the perimeter, is 3.5 km in length and was commenced around 1294. This massive building project not only had to work efficiently with the curves of the River Wensum and the existing

# GEOGRAPHY

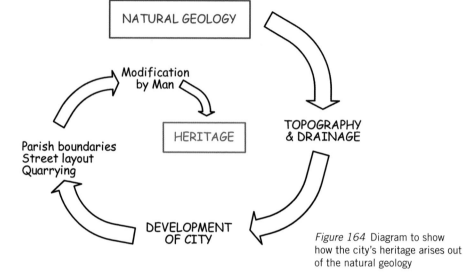

Figure 164 Diagram to show how the city's heritage arises out of the natural geology

gradients, it also seems deliberately to have skirted the heads of the valleys of the Great and Little Cockeys. There was originally a deep defensive ditch outside the wall which in places may have contained standing water, such as where it crossed the Dalymond valley, or where it was dug into brickearth. The planning and construction of the wall inevitably meant working with the grain of the city.

The notion of 'grain' has probably driven antiquarians for at least the last two centuries, but not all will have had the amount of factual detail we have today, leading them to have to speculate a little more over some alignments (Figure 166).

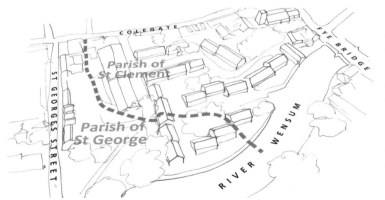

Figure 165 Sketch aerial view to show the route of a parish boundary from Colegate through what is now Friars Quay, perhaps marking the former course of the Muspole Stream

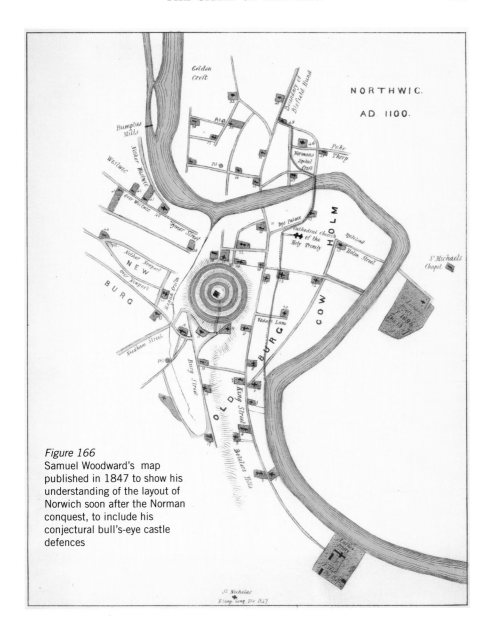

*Figure 166*
Samuel Woodward's map
published in 1847 to show his
understanding of the layout of
Norwich soon after the Norman
conquest, to include his
conjectural bull's-eye castle
defences

## Going against the grain

The late twentieth-century fad for motor cars, taking advantage of a brief period in human history when hydrocarbons were cheaply available, could be regarded as a significant intervention in the natural scheme of things. The need to provide road space required a fair amount of activity that usually ignored the grain of the city. This was brought into stark relief by the publication of the 1945 Norwich Plan by the City Corporation. Emerging from the debris of the Second World War, its approach to the city's transport infrastructure described a brave new world of cleared buildings and widened roads, a sleek and open 'motor city' both with ring roads and new wide highways passing through the city centre.

Figure 167 Illustration from the James, Pearce and Rowley *City of Norwich Plan* of 1945, showing a proposed high-level viaduct crossing from Bracondale to Thorpe Hamlet

Neither the slightly awkward geometry of the medieval street layout nor the gradient changes were an obstacle to the City of Norwich Plan: new concrete structures could solve all that, and motor vehicles are equipped with plenty of surplus power to deal with necessary climbs. So the plan envisaged dramatic additions such as a high-level viaduct sweeping majestically at an angle over King Street (Figure 167), a new Duke Street bridge aligned to the bottom of Exchange Street, and a completed inner ring road cutting inside (and even tunnelling below) the medieval core in places.

Mercifully, much of this never happened, but sadly the 'bulldoze and rebuild' mentality that pays scant regard or respect to the longstanding layout (and underlying reasons for it) did survive for another half-century. The obsession with motor travel led to mass demolitions in the 1960s associated with the construction of the inner ring road and Magdalen Street flyover. This mindset was also responsible for the distinctively post-war Rouen Road, and for a serious proposal by Norfolk County Council in the 1980s for a tunnel under Ber Street and angled flyover passing over King Street near Dragon Hall. That was only stopped following an outcry in Norwich and the plan subsequently failing at a public inquiry.

However, there continue to this day to be new road schemes implemented that blatantly go against the grain, often chopping across longstanding rectangular property

Figure 168 New Botolph Street, a link road constructed in 2010 as part of a new one-way system, curves randomly across all of the pre-existing urban grain

Figure 169
Anglia Square and
the inner ring road,
from the truncated
end of St George's
Street (renamed
New Botolph
Street) showing a
remnant of
unusable land

boundaries to leave small triangular spaces that are unusable and contribute nothing to the city. A recent example is New Botolph Street (Figure 168), even the name of which does not fit because it has no geometric relationship with the original Botolph Street, which was obliterated beneath the Anglia Square development in 1971. It remains to be seen to what extent the soon-to-be redeveloped Anglia Square will rediscover or recreate any of this original urban texture (Figure 169).

It is interesting to see the extent to which the medieval grain of the city has been reflected in one of the more recent maps published for Norwich – the city's Cycle Map. In the face of so many recent and profound diversions to the general road system for motor vehicles, it is perhaps no surprise that many of the cycle routes essentially follow the medieval network. This is because gradients and the conservation of effort played an equally strong part in the choice of route as for those pulling wheeled carts in medieval times. In fact the 2012 edition of the cycle map showed long cross-sections for the main colour-coded cycle routes (Figure 170), enabling the user to consider the gradient. (This innovative feature was sadly removed from the 2016 edition.) It is however ironic that the cycle routes do have to detour in places from the more direct routes in order to avoid heavily trafficked roads or one-way streets which are the legacy of the short-lived golden age of the motor car.

We could do worse than take the medieval layout as a starting-point if we are looking for ways of making a sustainable city.

## Recurring patterns

Beyond the physical manifestations of the city grain persisting in the line of roads or parish boundaries, we can also discern in places some longstanding patterns of influence, sometimes traceable across centuries, often recurring cyclically, and probably driven by topographic or other factors that are ultimately a product of the geology. These can arguably be regarded as expressions of the Principle of Uniformitarianism, and as such, two examples have already been described (see pages 3–7).

As another example, on the eastern approaches to the city centre at Yarmouth Road, there has always been very little space on the north side of the River Yare (which is at the northern edge of its wide flood plain) and the steep valley slope (which is composed

*Figure 170* The 2012 version of the Norwich Cycle Map included cross-sections (bottom of picture) to show the elevation and gradient of routes

of a sequence of layers from chalk, to crag, to glacial deposits). It was this naturally congested situation that forced the railway builders of the 1840s to put the rail line out on the flood plain, crossing the river twice on low bridges near the river green at Thorpe St Andrew and necessitating the New Cut to maintain navigation. With the mid-twentieth-century growth in motor traffic, a regular bottleneck developed at what became known as Thorpe Narrows (Figure 171), and in the early 1950s a number of dwellings close to the road on the opposite side to the Town House Hotel were demolished in order to widen the road substantially. Needless to say, in time the wide straight road became a safety problem because of speeding. Roll forward half a century, and what changes are made? The road is narrowed by central refuges (Figure 172), which now causes difficulty for wider vehicles and cyclists. Incidentally, another implication of this constricted corridor is that the road is insufficiently wide to accommodate a bus lane, thus undermining the attractiveness of the park-and-ride site at Postwick (intended to ease road congestion), the location of which was originally chosen because of potential rail access which never happened.

*Figure 171* The widening of Thorpe Narrows, Yarmouth Road in the 1960s, involving demolition of a number of buildings along the north side of the road

*Figure 172* Yarmouth Road today, complete with central refuges and speed reactive signs to reduce traffic speed

As a further example, the line of King Street at its outer end climbs up to join Braconedale at a level some 17 m higher than its lowest point. That is acceptable for those heading away from the city southwards onto higher ground (this is likely to be a pre-medieval walking route), but for those trying to get to a location further eastwards (down-stream) on the River Wensum (such as Trowse) it seems an unnecessary detour, in terms of both elevation and directness. This is a 'dog leg' that not only challenges cyclists trying to reach Whitlingham Park from the city centre: it also dictated the line of the original low-level sewer that had to get to Trowse (see pages 105–6) in the nineteenth century, necessitating the construction of access manholes some 20 m deep at the junction with Bracondale. The persistent reasons for not using the more direct route parallel to the river are geological and also tied in with the location of Colman's factory, which has occupied its riverside site since 1858. Interestingly, Samuel Woodward's conjectural map of early medieval Norwich drawn in 1847 (Figure 166, page 141) shows King Street taking a direct route parallel to the river at least as far as Carrow Priory, which stands on the Colman's site.

# 16
# Psychogeology

## The 'feel' of the city

The explanation given in Figure 164 (page 140) for the way people in Norwich have tended to behave over the centuries is probably self-evident, but more intriguing is the less tangible matter of how we feel – both in the city as a whole and also when in particular localities.

This line of thinking has been followed by students of 'psychogeography', a somewhat arty movement which crystallised in the 1950s, but which referred back to nineteenth-century activity in Paris, as well as to earlier work by William Blake and Daniel Defoe. Psychogeography has become increasingly popular in recent years, not least in Norwich, and lies behind the work of writers such as Peter Ackroyd on London, and his theory of chronological resonance. Guy Debord defined the subject as 'The study of the specific effects of the geographical environment, consciously organised or not, on the emotions and behaviour of individuals'. So he is adding emotion to mere behaviour, probably a response to the modern urban environment which (in Mervyn Coverley's words) 'seeks to overcome the process of banalisation'.

An obvious example of how geographical setting could affect emotions is the orientation of a valley side. A steep north-east-facing slope is likely to be rather darker, cooler and more overshadowed (especially in the winter) than a south-west-facing slope. If this is valid, it could for example influence the 'feel' of the Carrow Hill area in comparison with, say, St Leonard's Road.

Some people can be quite affected by the impact of large-scale changes in the layout of established parts of the city during redevelopment. An important factor in both civilised

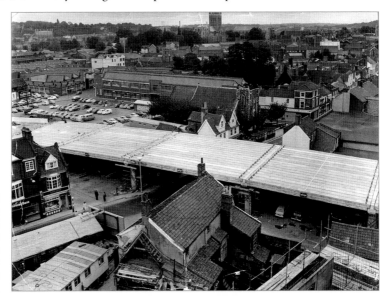

*Figure 173*
The controversial Magdalen Street flyover under construction in 1971

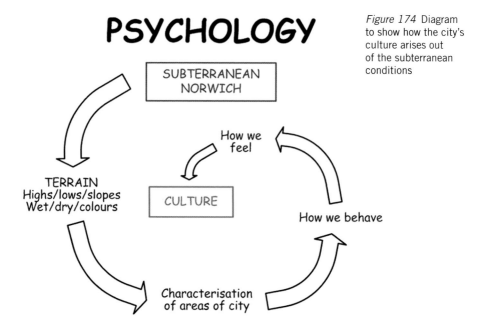

Figure 174 Diagram to show how the city's culture arises out of the subterranean conditions

society's acceptance and the long-term success of such schemes might be the degree to which they conform with the natural grain of the city. The insensitive decision to plough a new inner ring road east–west through the middle of Norwich Over the Water (the part of the medieval core north of the river) in 1970 is widely blamed for the subsequent four decades of environmental and social problems that have beset parts of the St Augustine's and Magdalen Street areas. These were the areas hived off from the medieval core by the link road (Figure 173) and dominated by the Anglia Square development. These changes paid no attention to the pre-existing grain (subtly trending north to north-west) and distorted the way in which people had moved through that part of the city for centuries. It is interesting to note that the Norwich Society, which opposed the original road scheme in the late 1960s, is now in favour of demolishing the Magdalen Street flyover and restoring (so far as is possible) the north–south links and the line of the original street frontages.

## Adding the fourth dimension

If you accept the linkage from the geographical environment to human emotions, it is possible to trace geological factors behind it (Figure 174). It may be fanciful, but we may perhaps be able to go a little further even than psychogeography, in that the model allows us to add the fourth dimension of time. Norwich is a good place where we could pursue a new specialist subject to be known as 'psychogeology' – whereby we would study the specific effects of the subterranean city, consciously organised or not, on the emotions and behaviour of individuals and the development of culture.

An example is Ber Street (Figure 175), which for centuries has had a slightly threatening reputation. It was known as 'blood-and-guts street', probably on account of the

*Figure 175* Ber Street on a misty winter's day. Is there something about this location that makes you feel differently from elsewhere in the city?

many butchers there near to the cattle market, and was where fiery Italian immigrants settled. Professional boxers grew up there, for some years it was the main red light district, and it is said policemen only went through in pairs. But think of the geological setting: Ber Street is perched on something of a ridge, with extensive excavation on the east side and chalk tunnels at depth. Could that be something to do with a feeling of 'edginess' and insecurity? Whether or not you accept such a linkage is up to you.

Many parts of the city are now greener and more dominated by trees than they were a hundred years ago. One such area is Harford Hills, a former chalk working on the slopes of the Yare Valley off Ipswich Road. The workings have left a legacy of a rather strange and undulating landscape (Figure 176). Understanding how this area looked as a working quarry, why it was there, and in particular seeing the faces of the men who worked there, can help to get us beyond this feeling of strangeness (Figure 177).

It may be that geology is only one of many factors contributing to our emotional response to certain parts of the city. It is however the case that a little digging to uncover possible reasons for feeling a certain way is a good first step towards overcoming any negative vibes we may be experiencing about a locality.

This approach to our emotional landscape may be at the outer edge of our quest to understand the place from ground level downwards, but it is surely better to seek reasons for the way things are than merely to treat the subterranean world as entirely inexplicable and mysterious. And in seeking understanding, there may well be more reasons for comfort than for fear.

I hope that throughout this book you have gained useful insights into the physical make-up of the ground beneath your feet in this particular city and how it may have changed over time. This is a depth of appreciation which has the potential to make any routine journey through Norwich more informative and worthwhile if you choose to lift your eyes. The smooth virtual world of your smartphone has its attractions, but so does the fascinating day-to-day reality of the grain of the subterranean city.

*Figure 176* Harford Hills today, now a wooded nature reserve

*Figure 177* Harford Hills in the late nineteenth century, a working chalk quarry, showing typical activities including tunnelling from worked chalk faces

# Further reading

## 1. Geological Norwich

Cox, F. C. et al. *Geology of the country around Norwich (Sheet Memoir 161)*. BGS, 1989.
Geological Survey Map *1:50,000 Sheet 161*, Norwich. BGS.
Holt-Wilson, T. *Norfolk's Earth Heritage*. Geo-Earth, 2010.
Larwood, G. P. et al. *The Geology of Norfolk*. Paramoudra Club, 1970.
Lee, J. R. et al. *British Regional Geology: East Anglia*. BGS, 2015.
Morton, J. *Strata: The Story of William Smith*. Brocken, 2004.
Woodward, H. B. *Geology of the Country around Norwich (memoir)*. HMSO, 1881.
www.bgs.ac.uk has many useful links, including geological and groundwater maps.

## 2. Norwich resculpted

Ayers, B. *Norwich: Archaeology of a fine city*. Amberley, 2009.
Campbell, J. *Norwich*. Historic Towns Trust and Scholar Press, 1975.
Frostick, R. *The Printed Plans of Norwich 1558–1840*. Frostick, 2002.
Jary, L. R. *Through Ancient Gates*. Larks Press, 2012.
Meeres, F. A. *History of Norwich*. Phillimore, 1998.
Rawcliffe, C. and Wilson, R. *Medieval Norwich*. A&C Black, 2006.
Storey, N. *Norwich: The Changing City*. Breedon, 2002.

## 3. Riddled with tunnels?

Atkin, M. 'The chalk tunnels of Norwich.' *Norfolk Arch.,* 1975.
Kelly, G. 'Underneath Norwich: chalk and flint workings.' NAHRG paper, 1994.

## 4. When things sink

Driscoll, R. and Skinner, H. *Subsidence Damage to Domestic Buildings*. BRE, 2007.
H. Humphreys & Partners. *Subsidence in Norwich*. HMSO, 1993.
Institution of Structural Engineers. *Subsidence of Low Rise Buildings*. IStrucE, 2000.

## 5. Geology drives everything

Coverley, M. *Psychogeography*. Pocket Essen., 2006.
James, C. H. and Pierce, S. R. *City of Norwich Plan 1945*. City of Norwich, 1945.
Nield, T. *Underlands: A journey through Britain's lost landscape*. Granta, 2014.

# Picture sources and credits

Grateful thanks are due to organisations and individuals for permission to reproduce figures as noted below.

Figures 3, 15 and 22 (*New Mills: Men Wading* by John Crome, 1812; *The Hill at Norwich on Market Day*, by Frederick Bacon Barwell, 1871; *Bishop's Bridge* by John Sell Cotman, c.1807): Norfolk Museums Service (Norwich Castle Museum and Art Gallery).

Figure 5 (Extract from Cole & Roper's map of Norwich of c.1807): Ian Fox collection.

Figure 8 (Dragon Hall archaeological excavation, 1998): copyright Norfolk County Council Historic Environment Service. Photograph by Jason Dawson.

Figures 11 and 159 (Sketch section by Samuel Woodward, 1833): courtesy of Christopher J. Wood, from *Geological Society of Norfolk Fiftieh Anniversary Jubilee Volume*, December 2000.

Figure 12 (South-eastward aerial view of the city centre, 2003): courtesy of Mike Page.

Figure 21 (Eastward view towards Thorpe Station and beyond, 1897): original Coe's image courtesy of Norfolk County Council Library and Information Service.

Figure 23 (View from St Leonard's Road, 1986): courtesy of Philip Marriage.

Figure 25 (the Gas Hill Gasp, 2013): mphotography.

Figures 26 and 27 (topographic maps): unknown Google source, now obsolete, with author's amendments.

Figures 44 (A former spring near Bishop's Bridge) and 49 (part: engraving from a drawing by Charles Catton Junior of 1792): illustrations from *Old Norwich*, Cotman & Hawcroft, 1961.

Figures 51 (Bomb crater, April 1942) and 173 (The Magdalen Street flyover, 1971): courtesy Archant CM Ltd.

Figure 54 (Early stages during constuction of Castle Mall, 1990), 77 (part: former brick field at Queen's Road in 1986), 94 (Flood level plate at New Mills Yard, 1961), 138 (Castle Mall under construction, 1992): by George Plunkett, courtesy of Jonathan Plunkett.

Figure 57 (Brushwood surface exposed in 1979): copyright Norfolk County Council Historic Environment Service. Photograph by Ray Britt.

Figures 63 (part: St Peter's Street in the 1890s), 96 (Southward view towards the rear of houses fronting Heigham Street, 1912), 97 (part: Norwich Mercury Works in 1912), 103 (50 Merton Road, 1936), 117 (part: tunnel entrances off Rosary Road in the late ninteenth century), 140 (Duke's Palace, early 1700s), 177 (Harford Hills in the late nineteenth century): courtesy of Norfolk County Council Library and Information Service.

Figures 65 and 163 (William Cunningham's prospect of Norwich of 1558): public domain image.

Figure 68 (Cross-section from a plan of 1886): Norfolk Record Office, City Engineer's deposited plans, N/EN 24/19.

Figures 78 (postcard of around 1905), 90 (engraving by Samuel and Nathaniel Buck, 1741), 92 (Thomas Cleer's map of 1696): public domain images from the author's collection.

Figure 87 (The stone bridge at Horsefair, 1888): courtesy Norfolk & Norwich Archaeological Society.

Figure 89 (Nineteenth century hand bill): public domain image sourced from Joyce Gurney-Read, *Trades and Industries of Norwich*, 1988.

Figure 91 (Carrow Maltings under demolition, 2003): 19 April 2012 post on The PinkUn Forum, Lord Horn.

Figure 100 (The bus-in-hole incident, 1988): Wikimedia Commons, uploaded by mira66.

Figure 101 (The incident as it looked to a passer-by on Earlham Road, 1988): courtesy Helen Cocksedge.

Figures 102 and 111 (local press coverage, 1988 and 1990): courtesy Archant – *Eastern Evening News*.

Figure 104 (Merton Road collapse, 1927): Phyllis Gladwell collection.

Figure 105 (local press article, 1930): courtesy Archant – *Eastern Daily Press*.

Figure 106 (Earlham Road mine plan) incorporates published layout courtesy of Archant and *Eastern Daily Press* and data from a paper by G. J. Smith and M. S. Rosenbaum in *Quarterly Journal of Engineering Geology*, vol. 26, pp. 281–91, 1993.

Figure 113 (cross-section of Assembly House): photograph of architectural drawing on display.

Figure 114 (Undercroft at the Assembly House): courtesy Terry George.

Figure 116 (Thorpe Hamlet hillside in July 1932): copyright Historic England.

Figure 118 (Interior of tunnel off Rosary Road): courtesy Alex George.

Figure 122 (sewerage system): adapted by the author from a City of Norwich publication, *Sewage Purification Works, Whitlingham*, 1963.

Figures 123, 124 and 125 (cross-section, sewers, pre-1960s and 1960s): from a City of Norwich/ IoME publication, *Riverside Intercepting Sewer*, undated.

Figure 128 (Map showing land uplift and subsidence): courtesy Ian Shennan/*GSA Today*, Vol. 19, Issue 9, September 2009.

Figure 133 (Painting of a paramoudra): adapted by the author from an illustration licensed under Creative Commons.

Figure 139 (part): Castle Mall in early stages of construction, 1991): copyright Norfolk County Council Historic Environment Service. Photograph by Neil Moss. (Part: plan of solution features) courtesy of Bovis Civil Engineering, sourced from H. Humphreys & Partners, *Subsidence in Norwich*, 1993.

Figure 142 (The Nest football ground, 1908): Dick Middleton/Paul Standley collection.

Figure 152 (Part of a hazard map): courtesy of Clive Edmonds, adapted from *Quarterly Journal of Engineering Geology*, Vol. 16, pp. 261–6, 1983.

Figure 157 (Concrete piles being driven for Dolphin Footbridge in 1909): Colin Proctor/Paul Standley postcard collection.

Figure 160 (Cut made through buildings in 1899): public domain image taken from Jonathan Mardle, *Victorian Norfolk*, 1981.

Figure 166 (Samuel Woodward's map, 1847): from *The History and Antiquities of Norwich Castle*, 1847, author's collection.

Figure 167: from James, Pearce and Rowley's *City of Norwich Plan*, 1945.

Figure 170 (The 2012 version of the Norwich Cycle Map): courtesy Norwich City Council.

Figure 171 (The widening of Thorpe Narrows, 1960s): George Swain image, courtesy of Norfolk County Council Library and Information Service.

Where not otherwise noted, photographs and drawings are by the author.

The author and the publishers have made every effort to ensure that all necessary permissions have been obtained for the material reproduced in this book, but if any omissions are brought to their attention, they will be happy to rectify them in future editions.

# Index

Note: streets and buildings in Norwich are indexed individually. General aspects related directly to the city are indexed under 'Norwich'. Individual churches are indexed under 'churches', bridges under 'bridges', rivers under 'rivers'. References to illustrations (including the sites from which they were taken) are in **bold**.

For details of these and our other fine illustrated books visit

# www.lassepress.com